EASY PIANO

LA LA LA[ND]

MUSIC FROM THE MOTION PICTURE SOUNDTRACK

CW00664771

First published in 2017 by Faber Music Ltd
Bloomsbury House
74–77 Great Russell Street
London WC1B 3DA
Printed in England by Caligraving Ltd

ISBN10: 0-571-53983-1
EAN13: 978-0-571-53983-3

To buy Faber Music publications or to find out about the full range of titles available
please contact your local music retailer or Faber Music sales enquiries:

Faber Music Limited, Burnt Mill, Elizabeth Way, Harlow, CM20 2HX England
Tel: +44 (0)1279 82 89 82 Fax: +44 (0)1279 82 89 83
sales@fabermusic.com fabermusicstore.com

ANOTHER DAY OF SUN

Music by JUSTIN HURWITZ
Lyrics by BENJ PASEK & JUSTIN PAUL

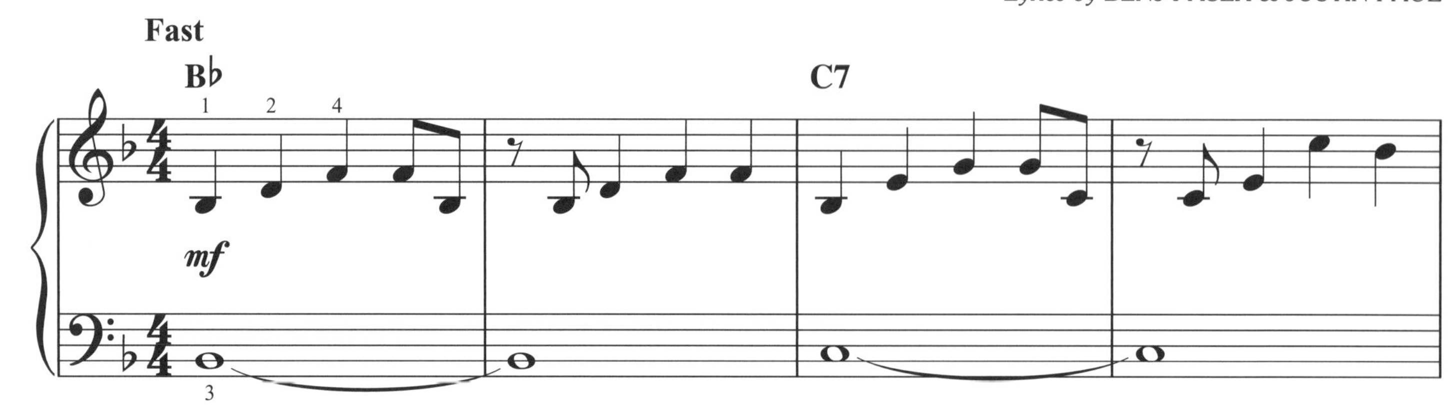

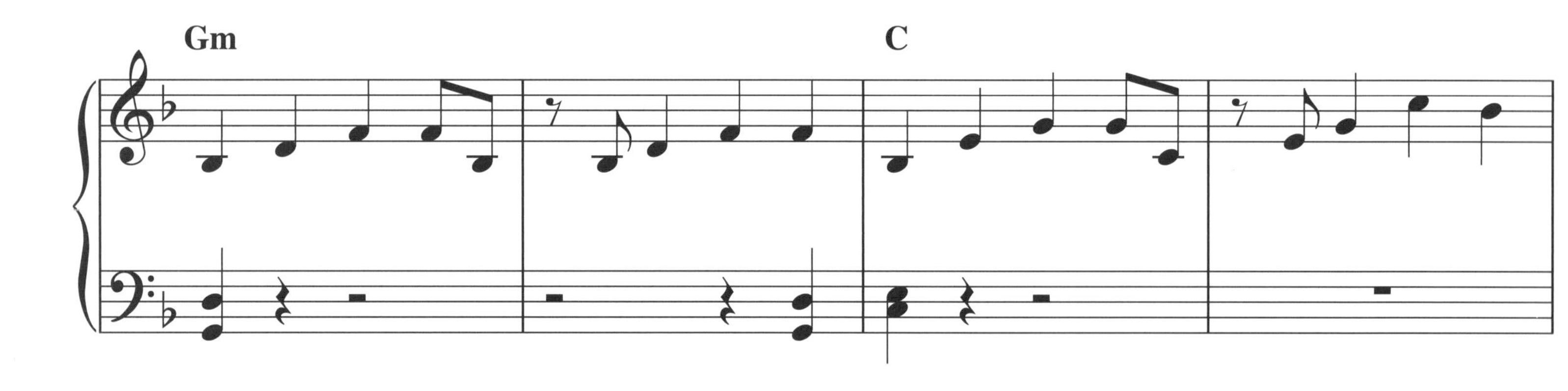

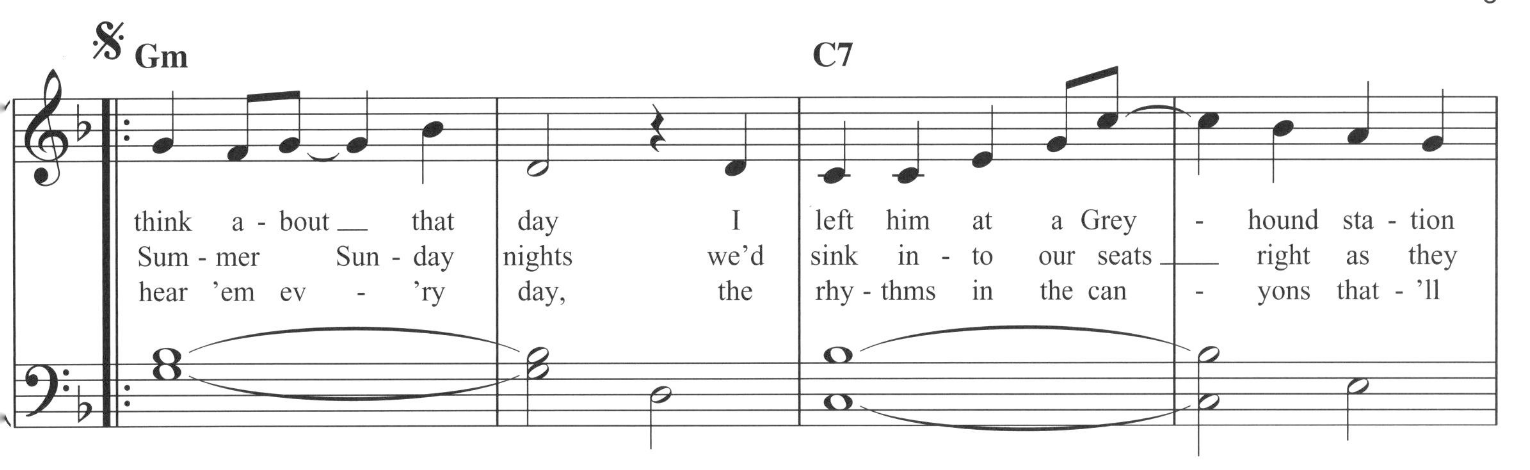
Gm
C7
think a - bout that day I left him at a Grey - hound sta - tion
Sum - mer Sun - day nights we'd sink in - to our seats right as they
hear 'em ev - 'ry day, the rhy - thms in the can - yons that - 'll

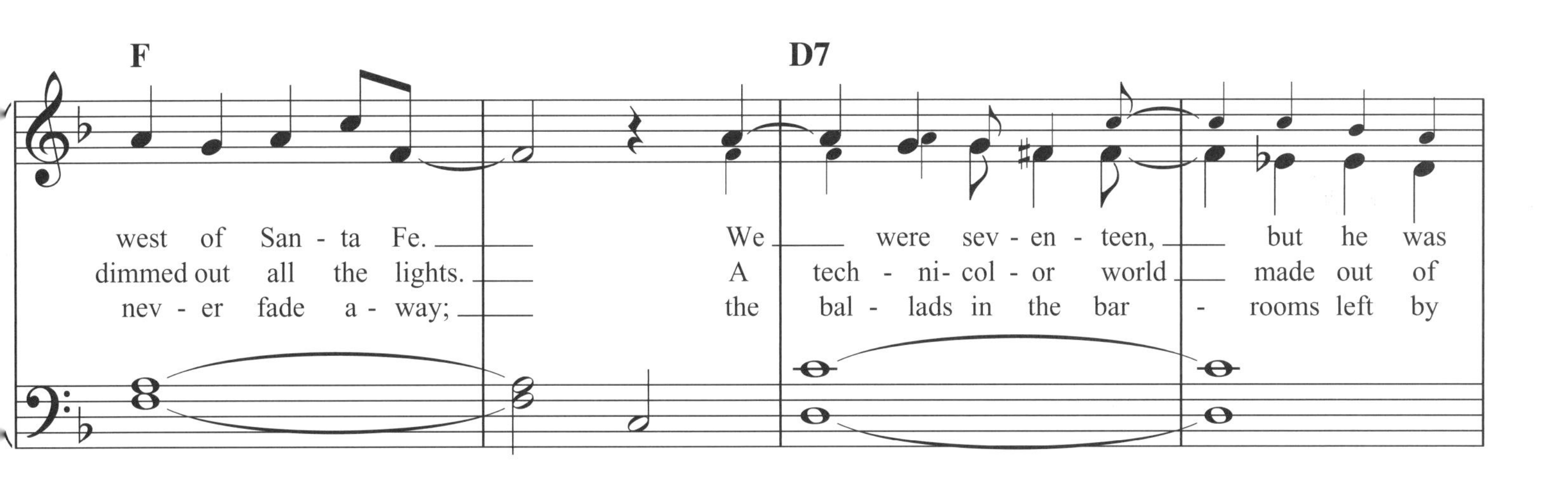
F
D7
west of San - ta Fe. We were sev - en - teen, but he was
dimmed out all the lights. A tech - ni- col - or world made out of
nev - er fade a - way; the bal - lads in the bar - rooms left by

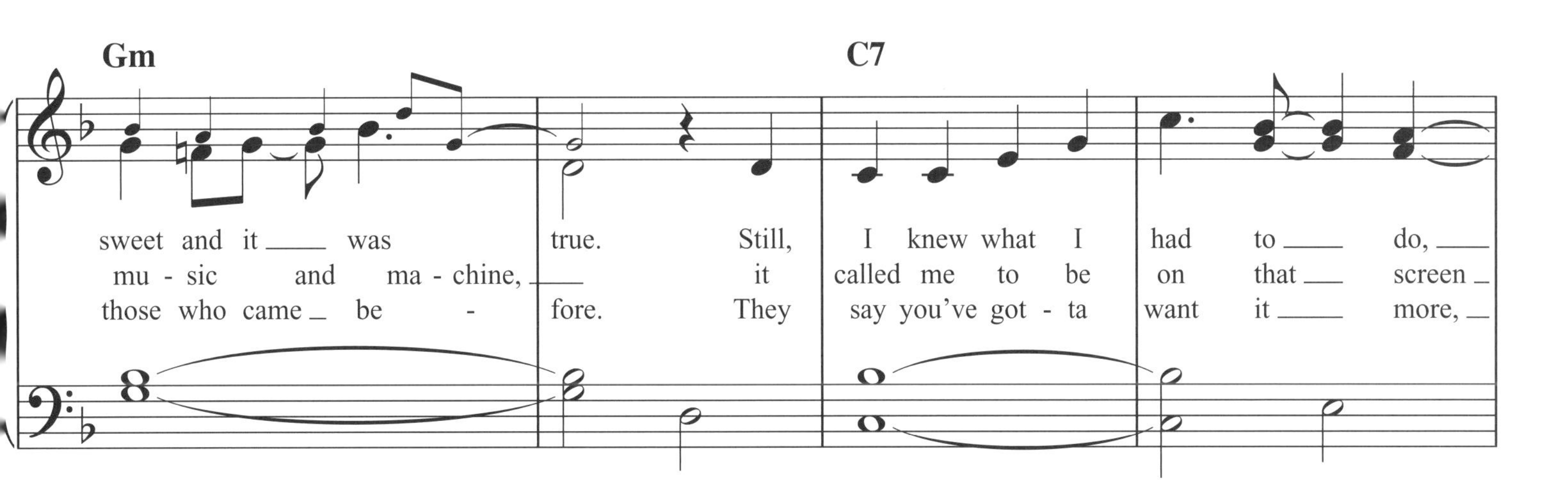
Gm
C7
sweet and it was true. Still, I knew what I had to do,
mu - sic and ma - chine, it called me to be on that screen
those who came be - fore. They say you've got - ta want it more,

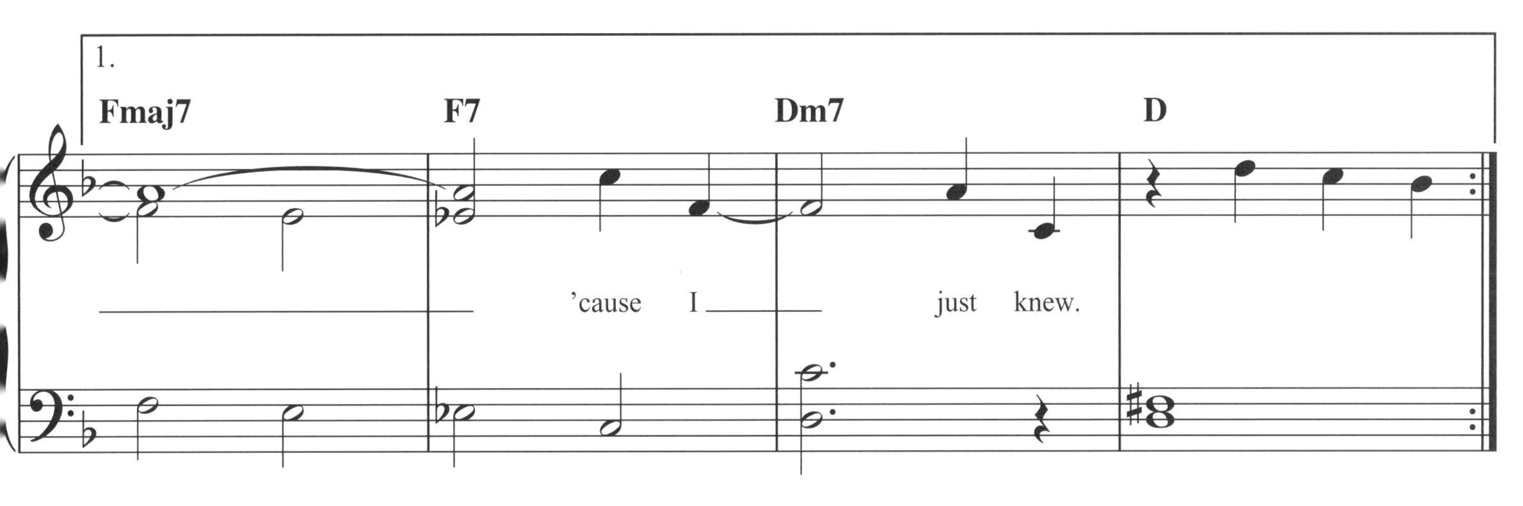
1.
Fmaj7
F7
Dm7
D
'cause I just knew.

2.,3.
F
Dm7
D7
and live in - side each scene. With -
so I bang on ev - 'ry door. And

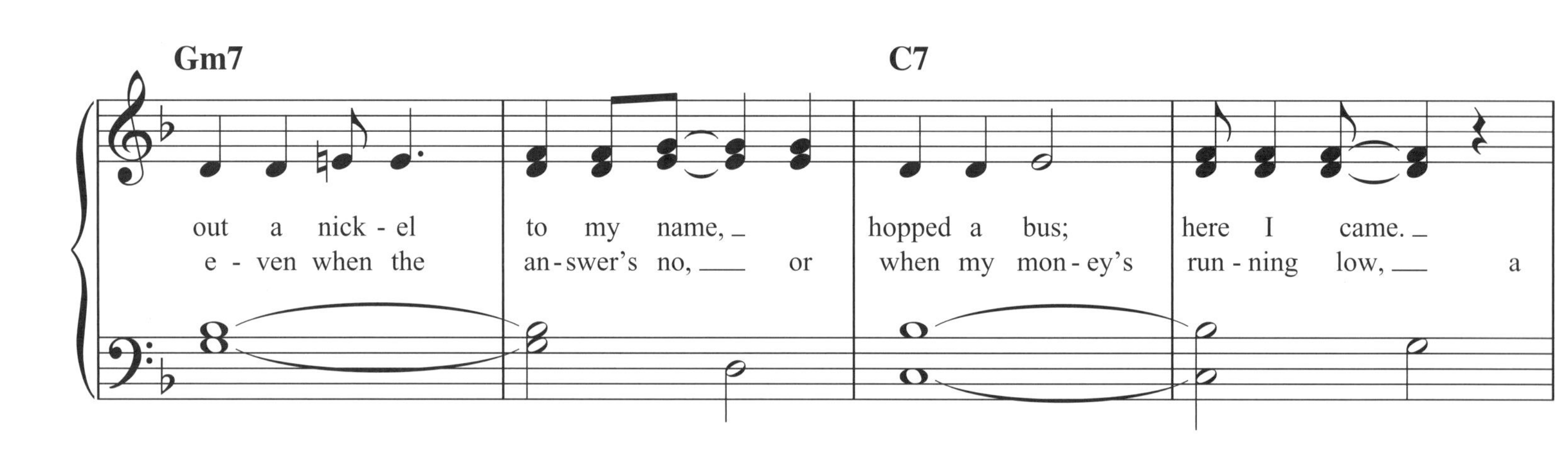
Gm7
C7
out a nick - el to my name, hopped a bus; here I came.
e - ven when the an-swer's no, or when my mon-ey's run-ning low, a

Dm
B♭
A7
Could be brave, or just in - sane. We'll have to see. 'Cause
dust - y mic and ne - on glow are all I need. And

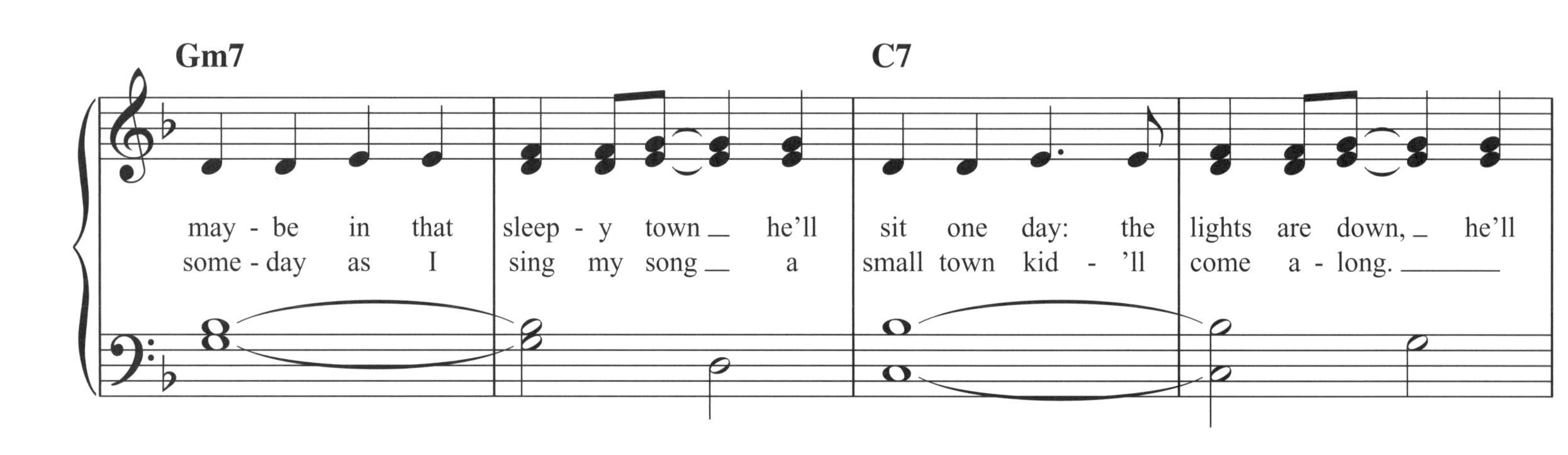
Gm7
C7
may - be in that sleep - y town he'll sit one day: the lights are down, he'll
some - day as I sing my song a small town kid - 'll come a - long.

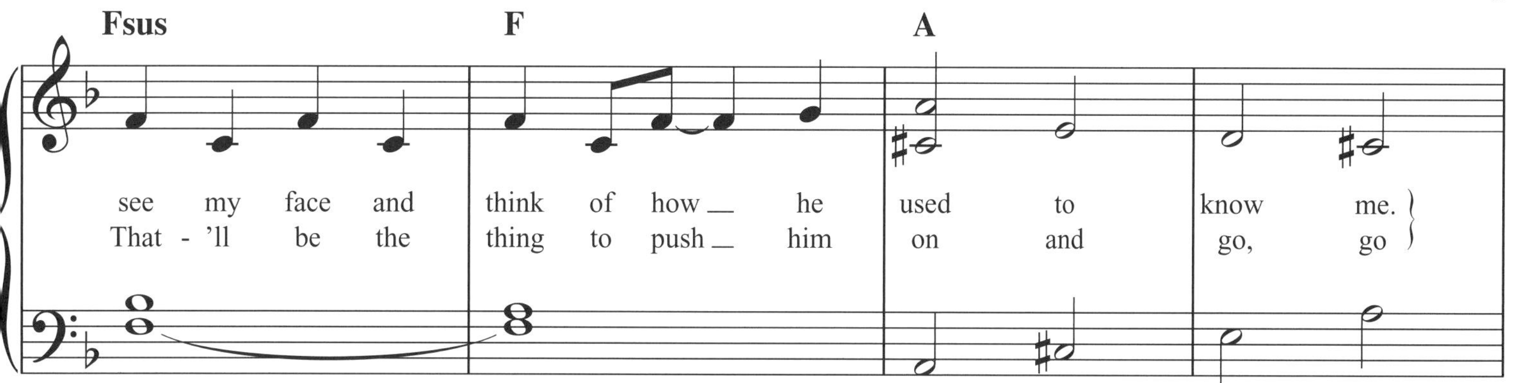
Fsus
F
A
see my face and think of how he used to know me.
That - 'll be the thing to push him on and go, go

B♭
C
F
Climb these hills, I'm reach - ing for the heights and

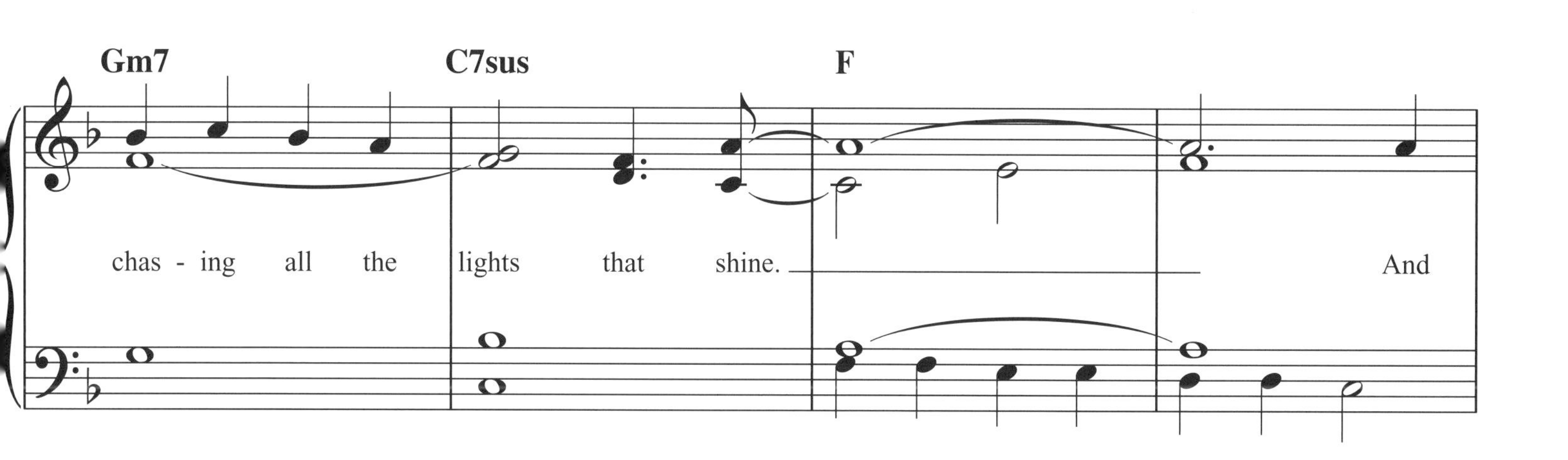
Gm7
C7sus
F
chas - ing all the lights that shine. And

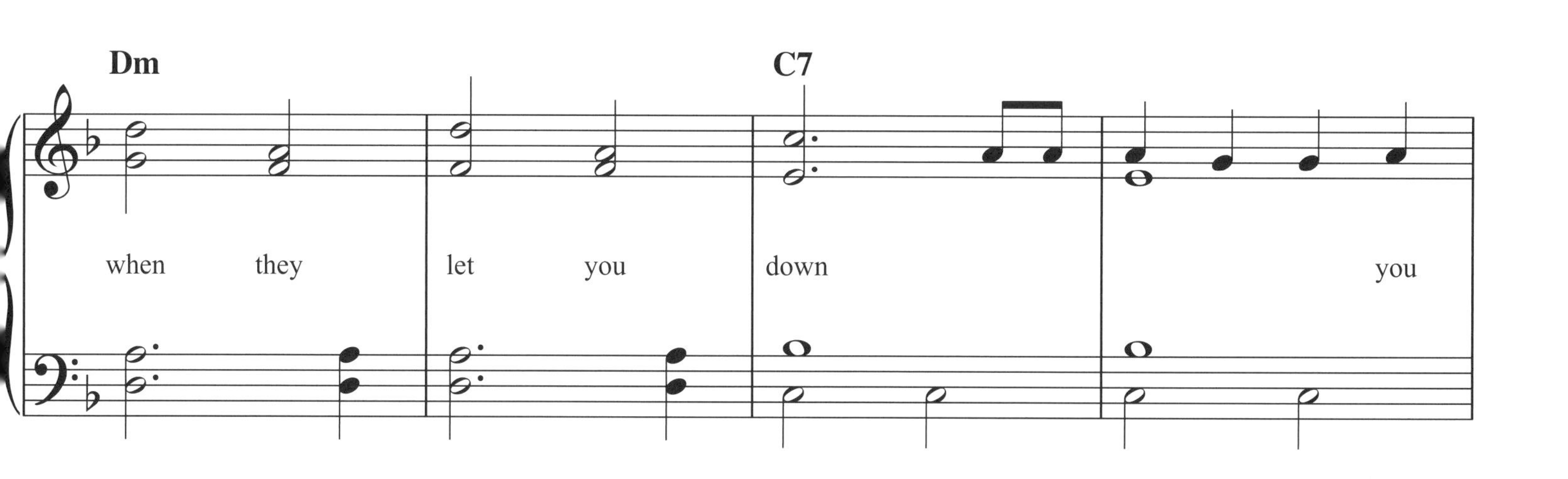
Dm
C7
when they let you down you

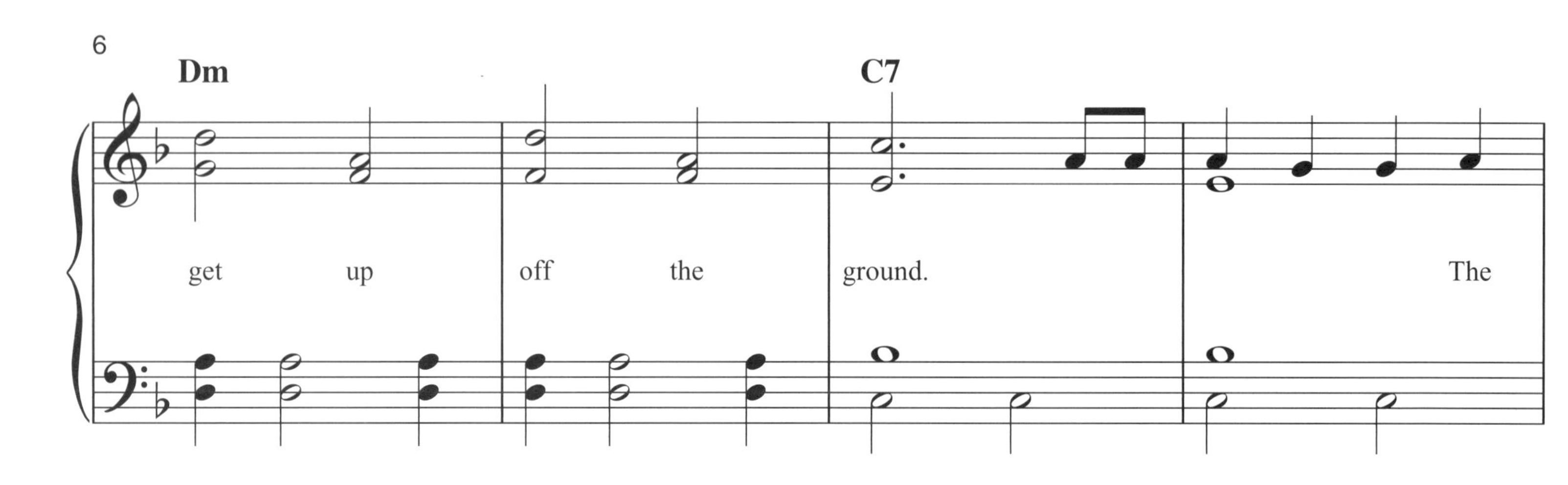
Dm
C7
get up off the ground. The

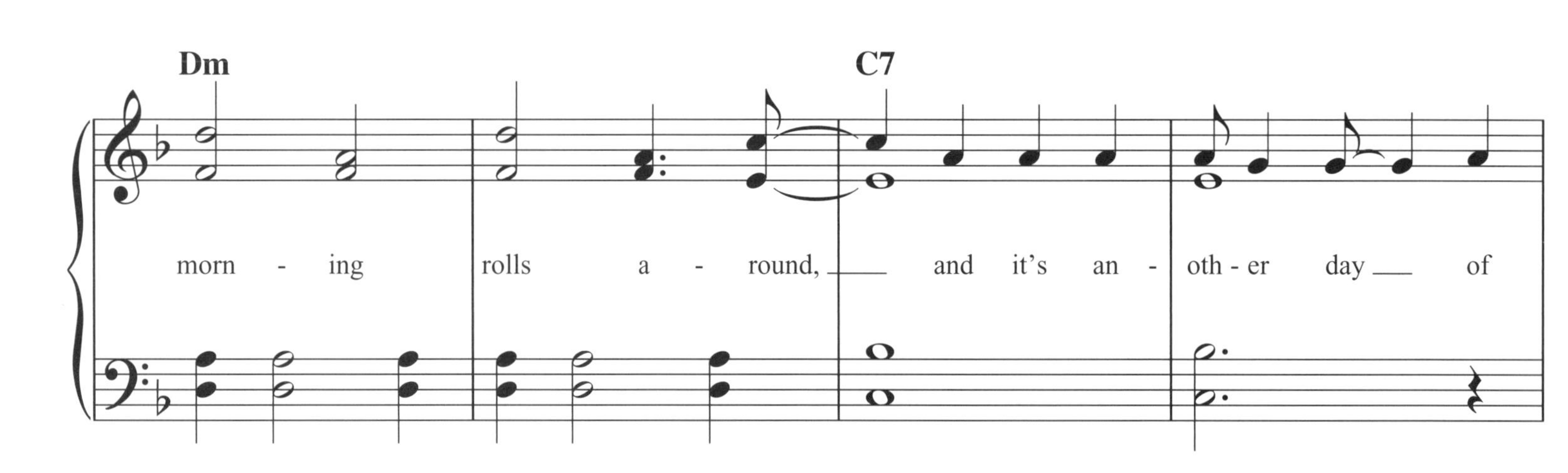
Dm
C7
morn - ing rolls a - round, and it's an - oth - er day of

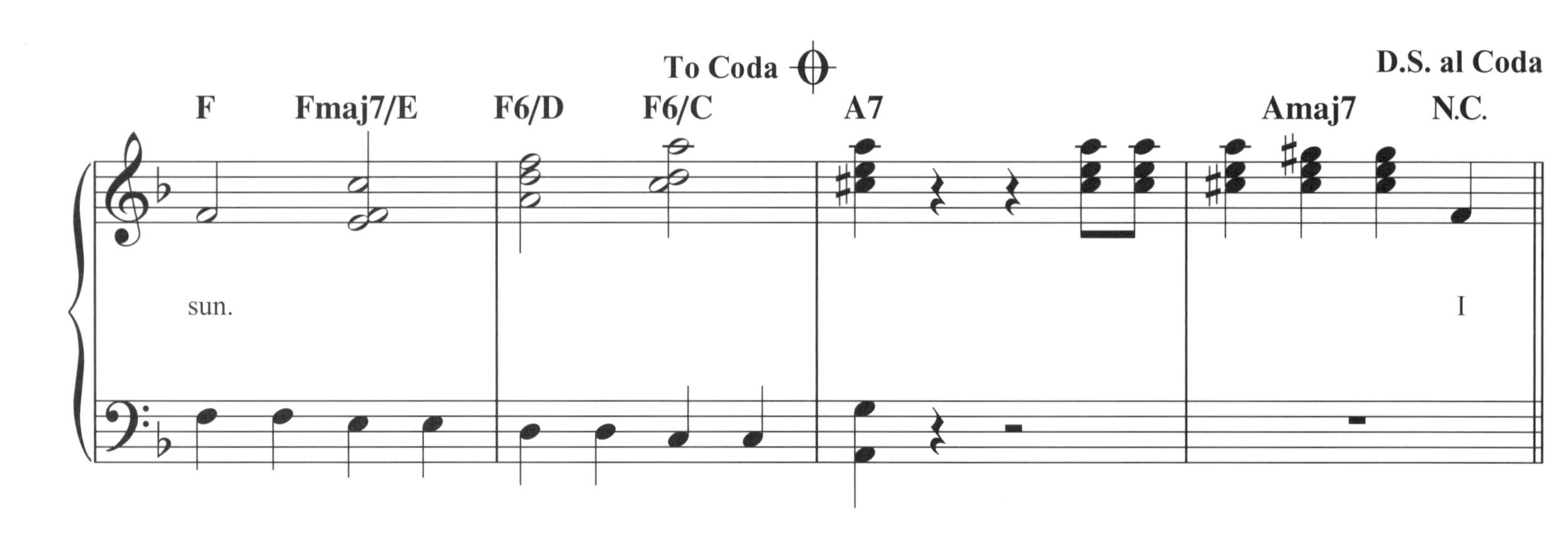
To Coda
D.S. al Coda
F Fmaj7/E F6/D F6/C A7 Amaj7 N.C.
sun. I

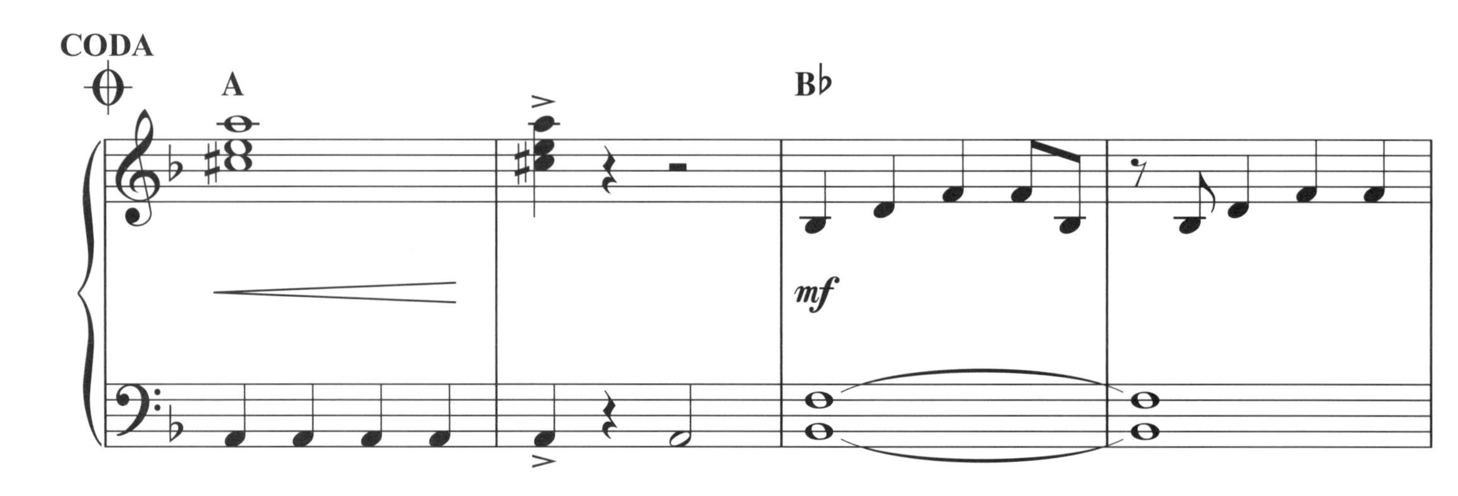
CODA
A
B♭
mf

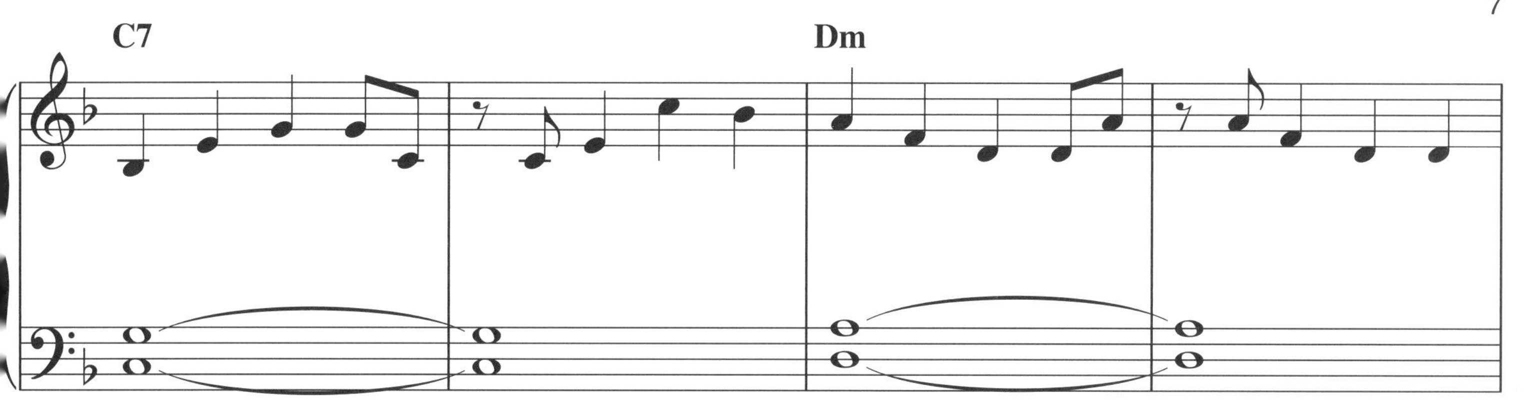
C7
Dm

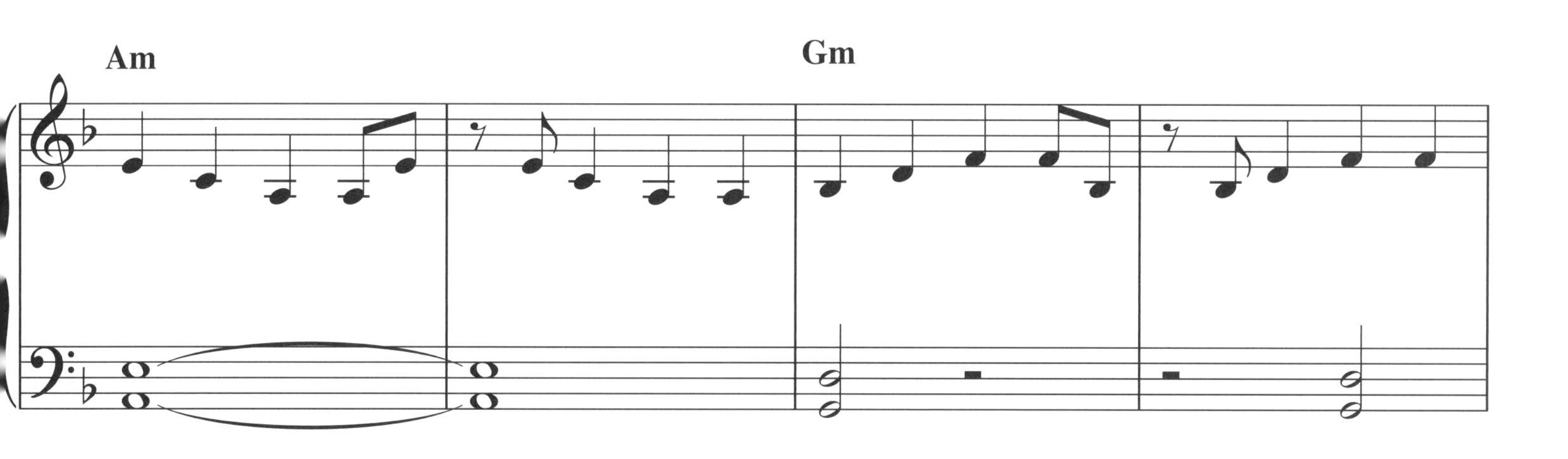
Am
Gm

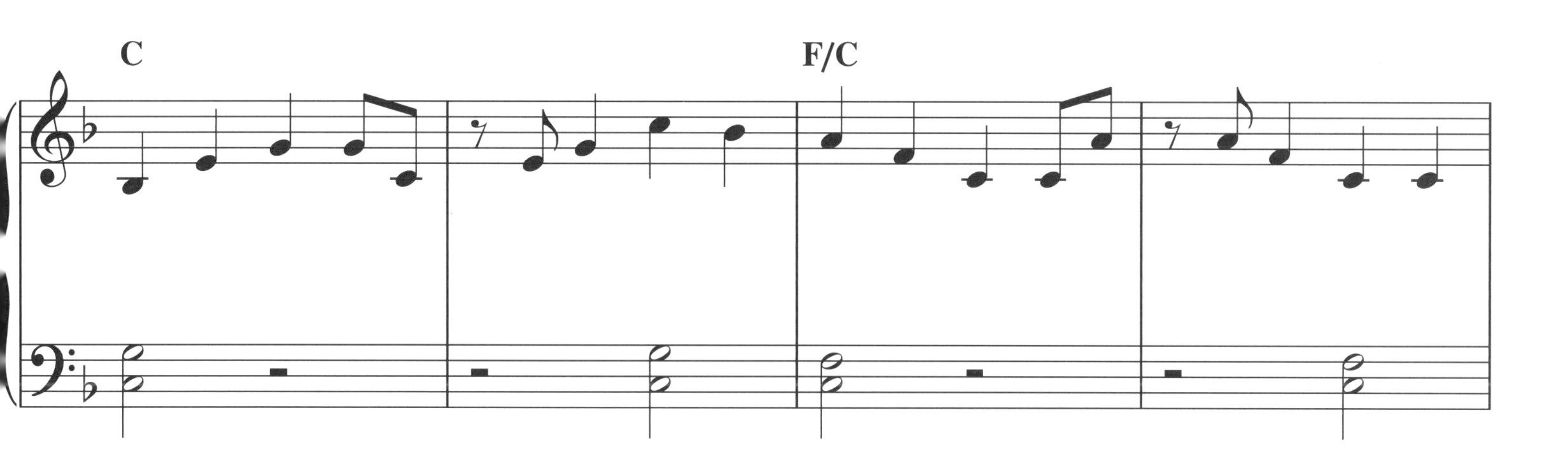
C
F/C

Am
N.C.
And
when
they
let
you

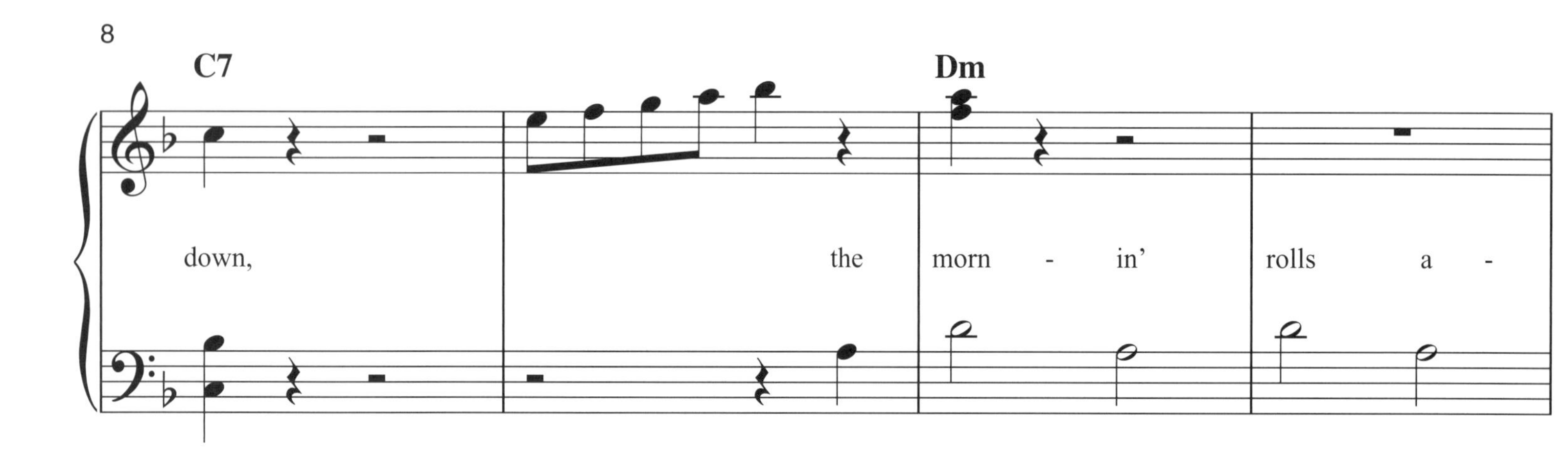
C7
Dm
down, the morn - in' rolls a -

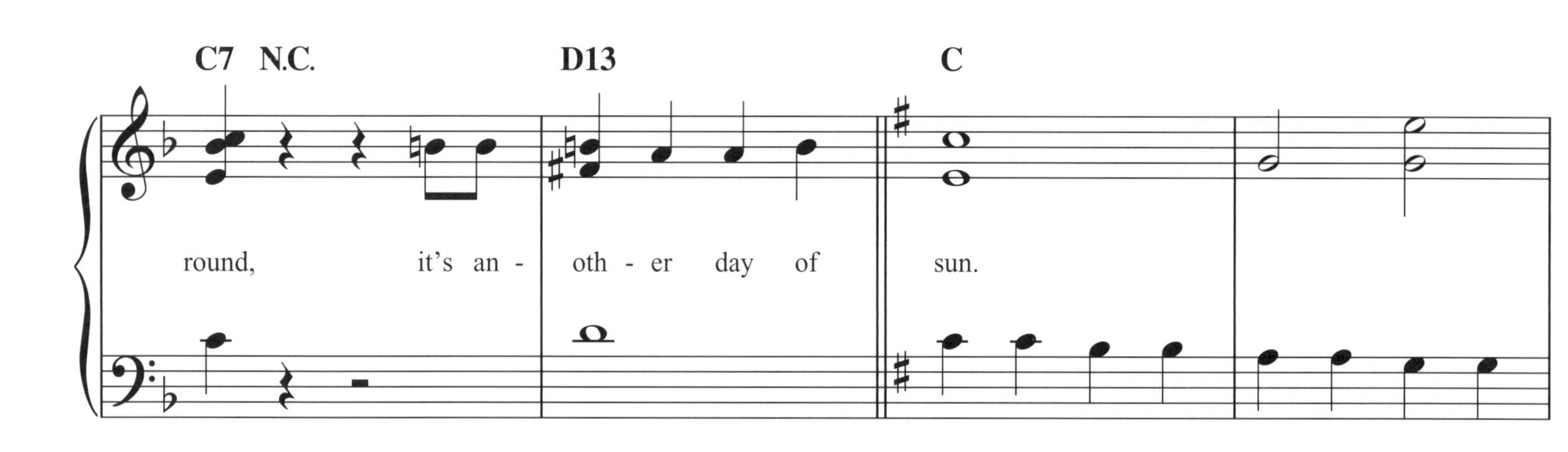
C7 N.C.
D13
C
round, it's an - oth - er day of sun.

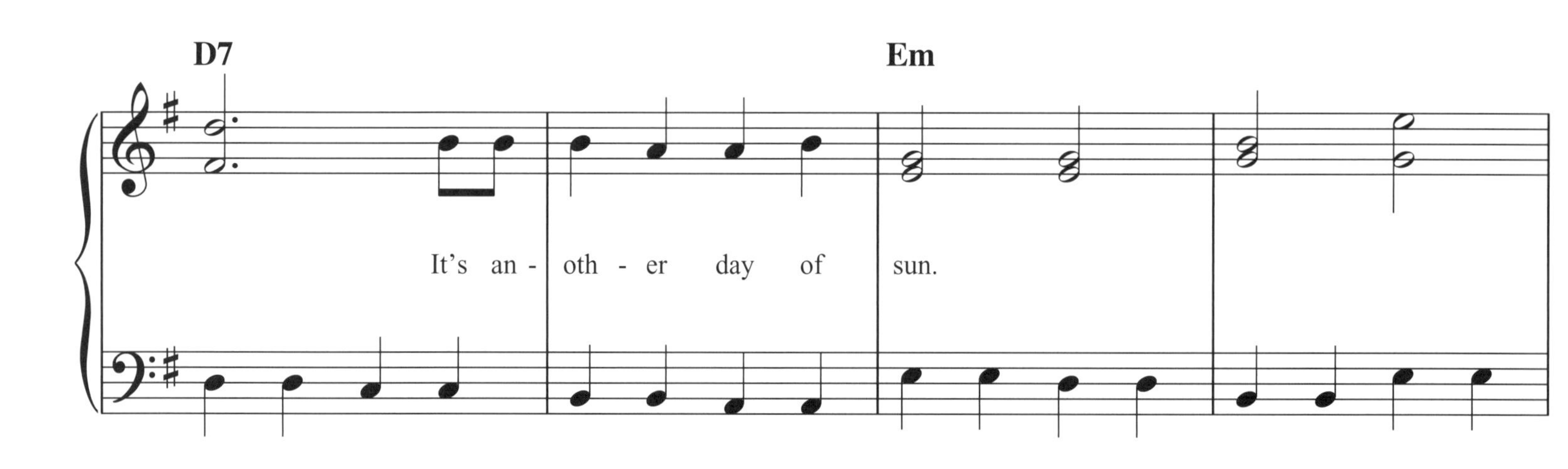
D7
Em
It's an - oth - er day of sun.

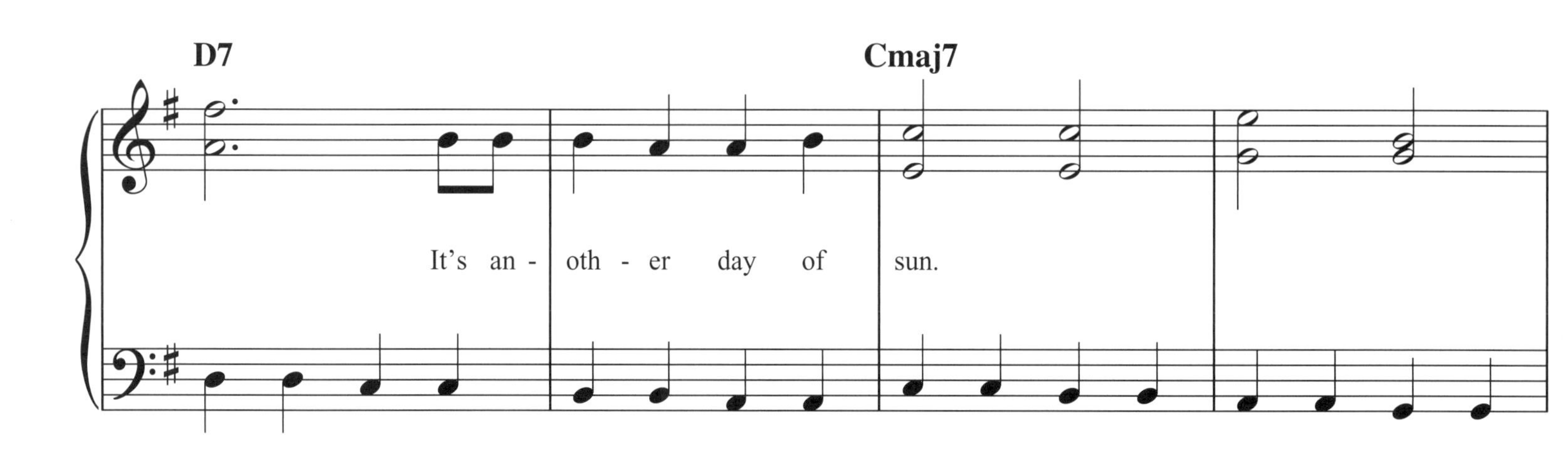
D7
Cmaj7
It's an - oth - er day of sun.

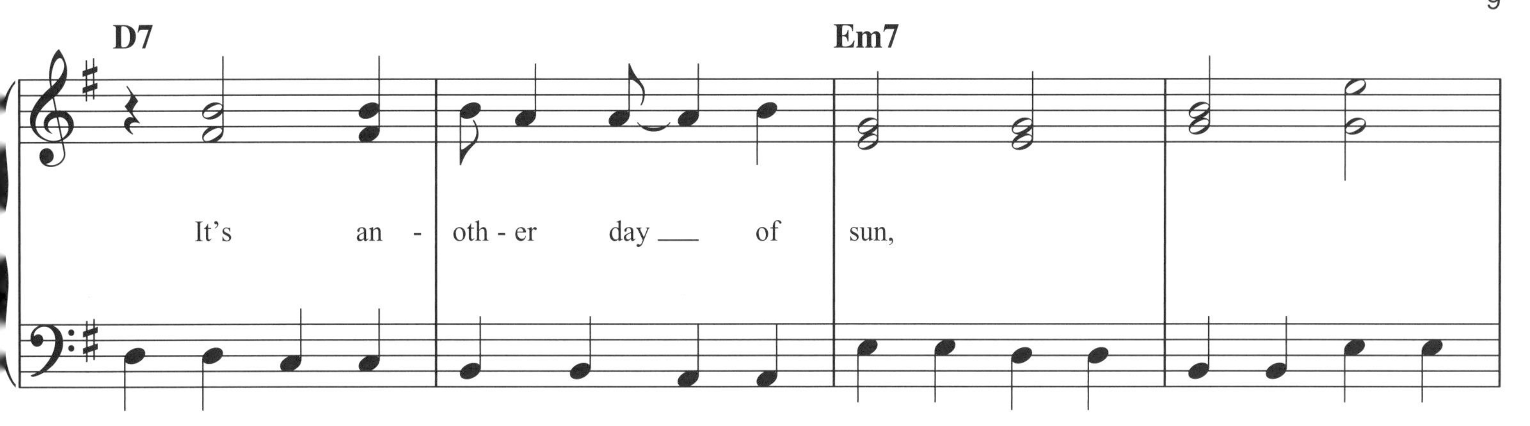
D7
Em7
It's an - oth - er day of sun,

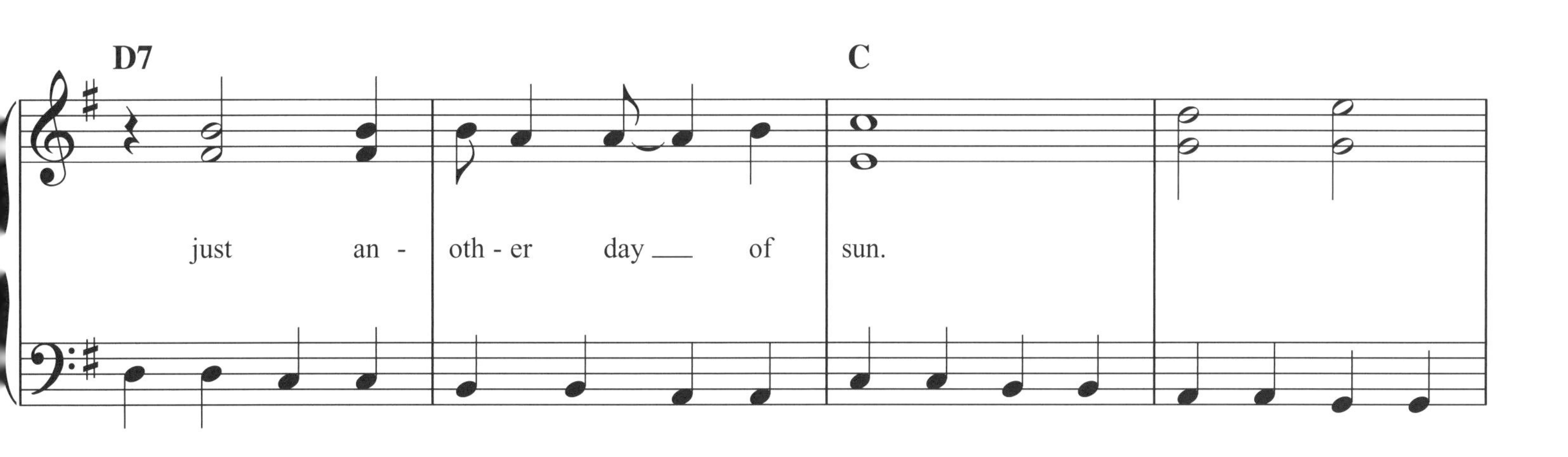
D7
C
just an - oth - er day of sun.

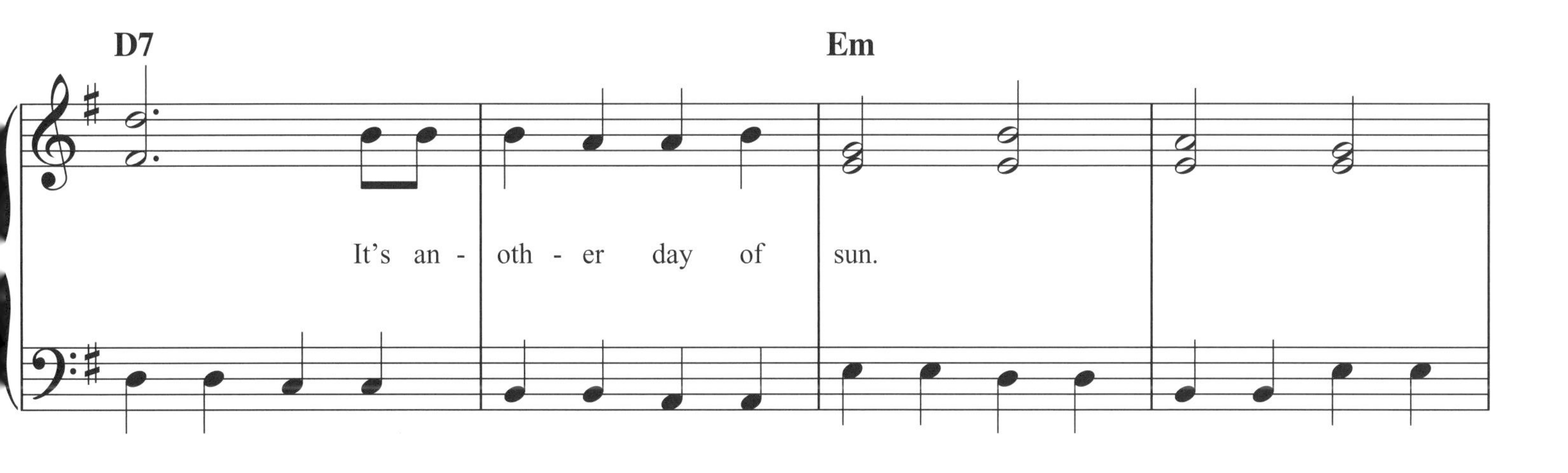
D7
Em
It's an - oth - er day of sun.

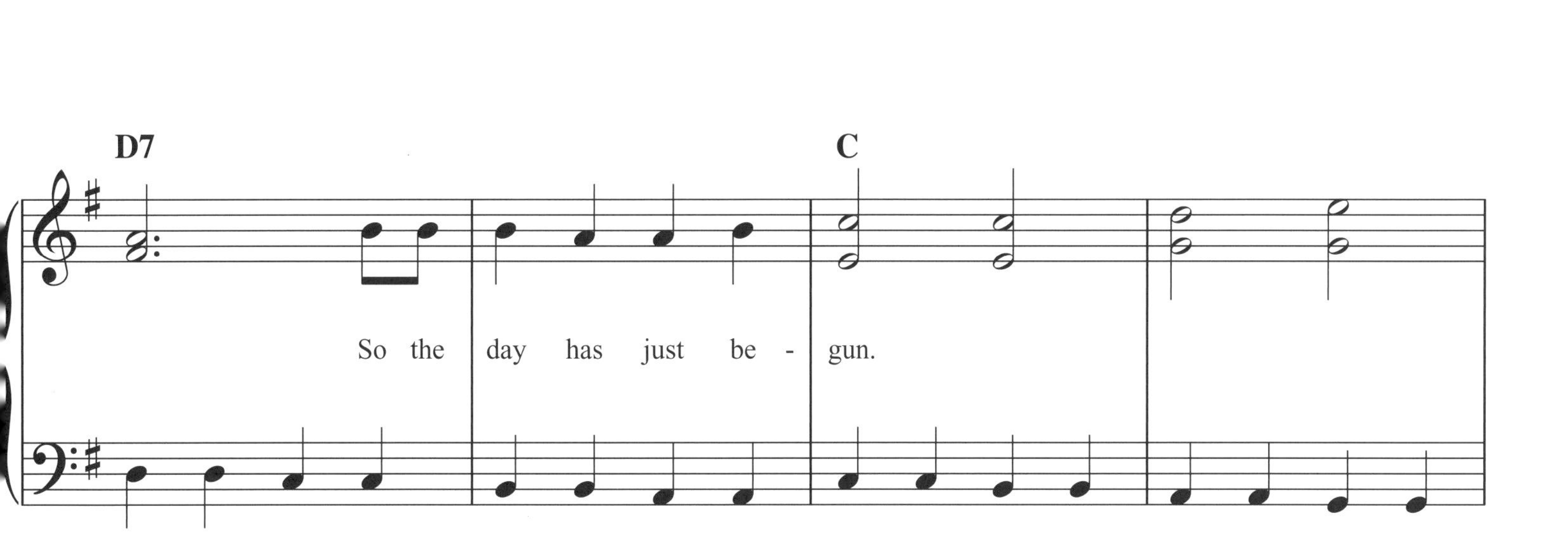
D7
C
So the day has just be - gun.

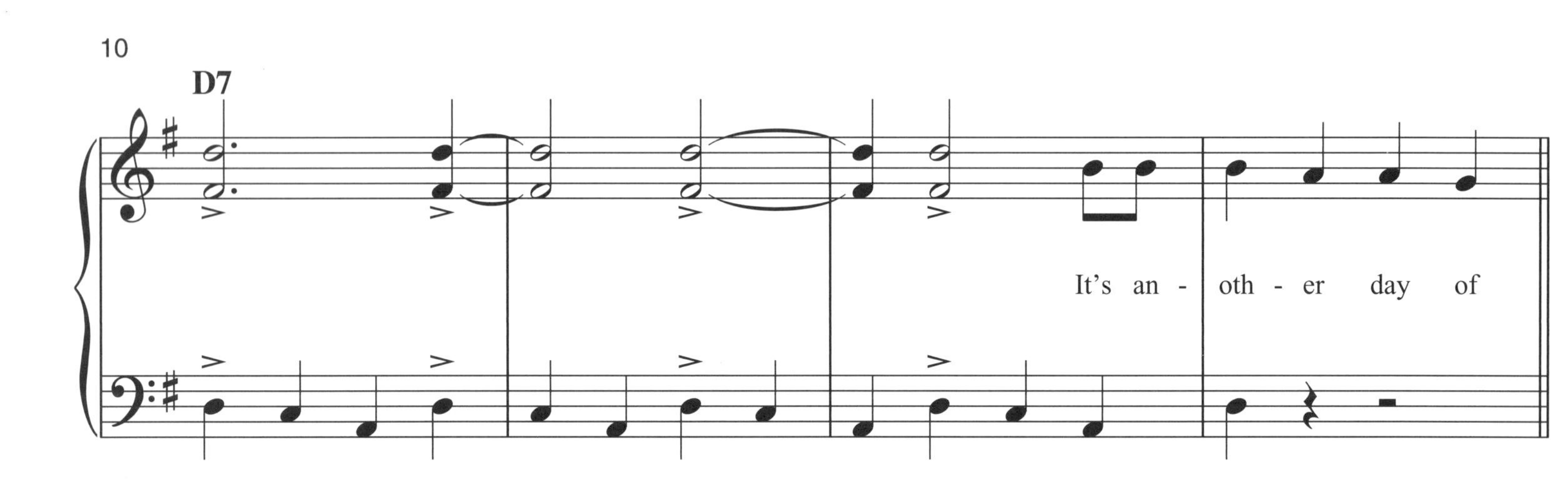
D7
It's an - oth - er day of

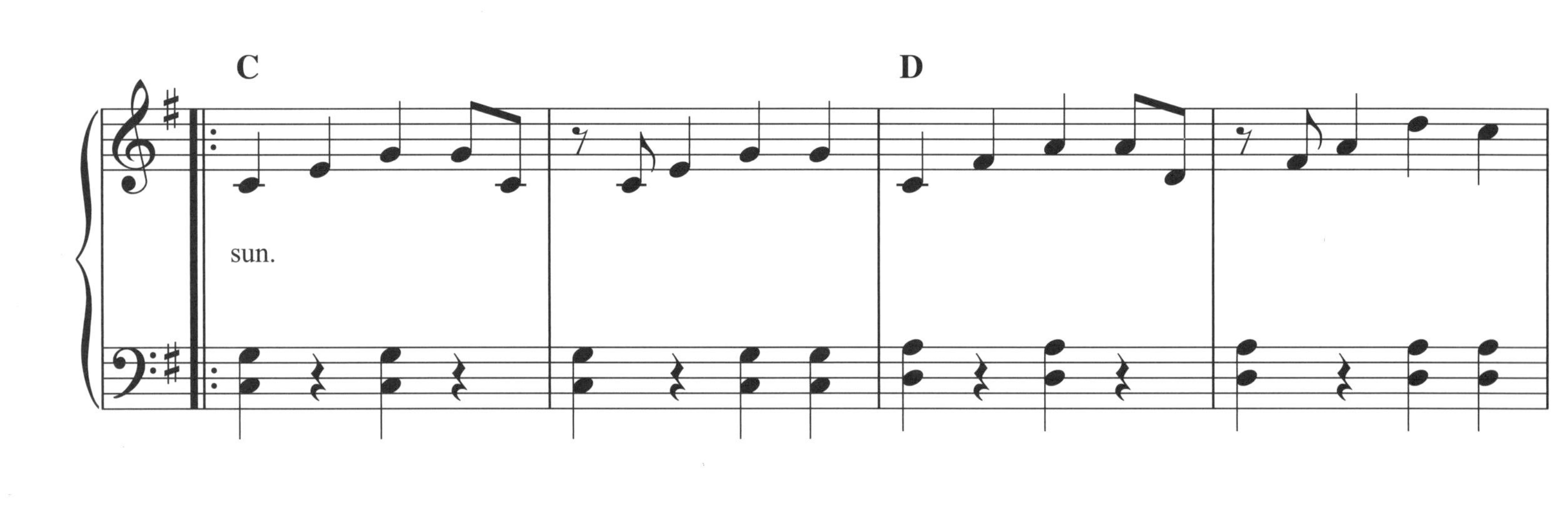
C
D
sun.

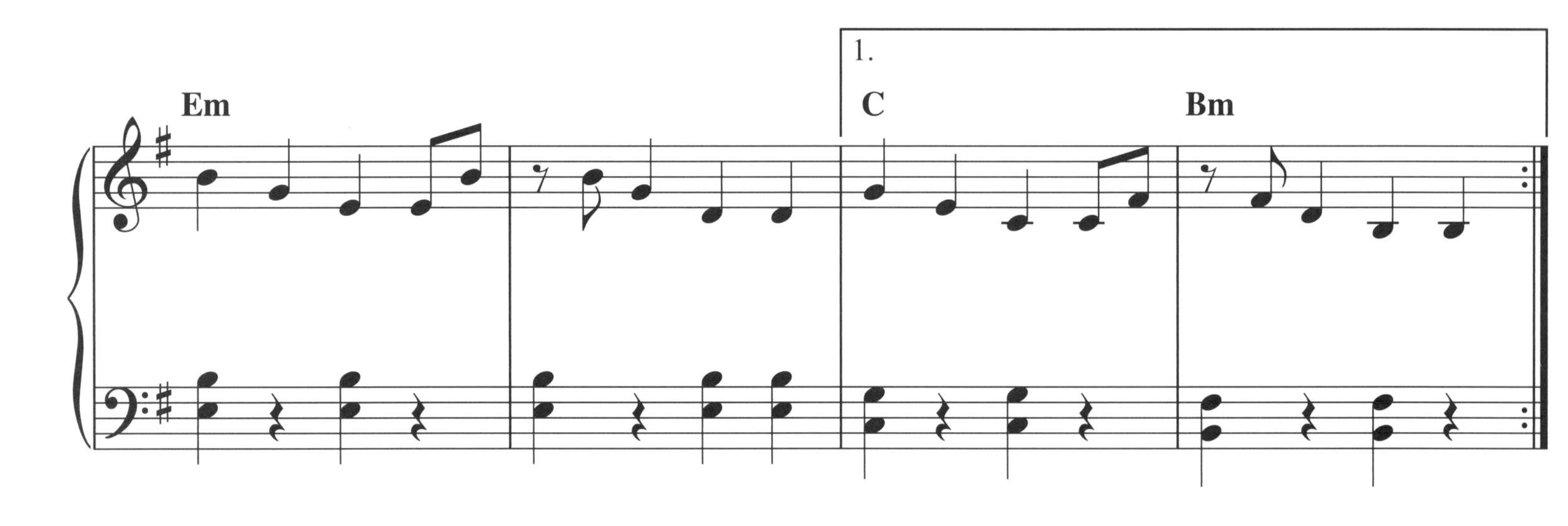
Em
1.
C
Bm

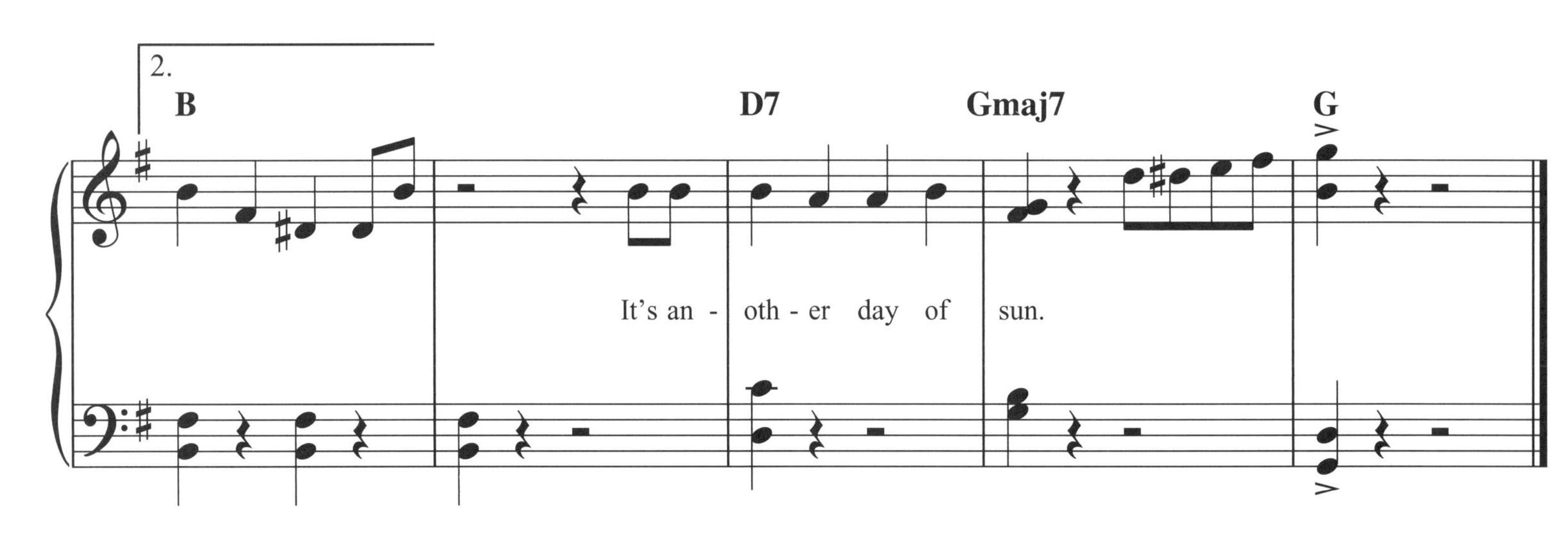
2.
B
D7
Gmaj7
G
It's an - oth - er day of sun.

SOMEONE IN THE CROWD

Music by JUSTIN HURWITZ
Lyrics by BENJ PASEK & JUSTIN PAUL

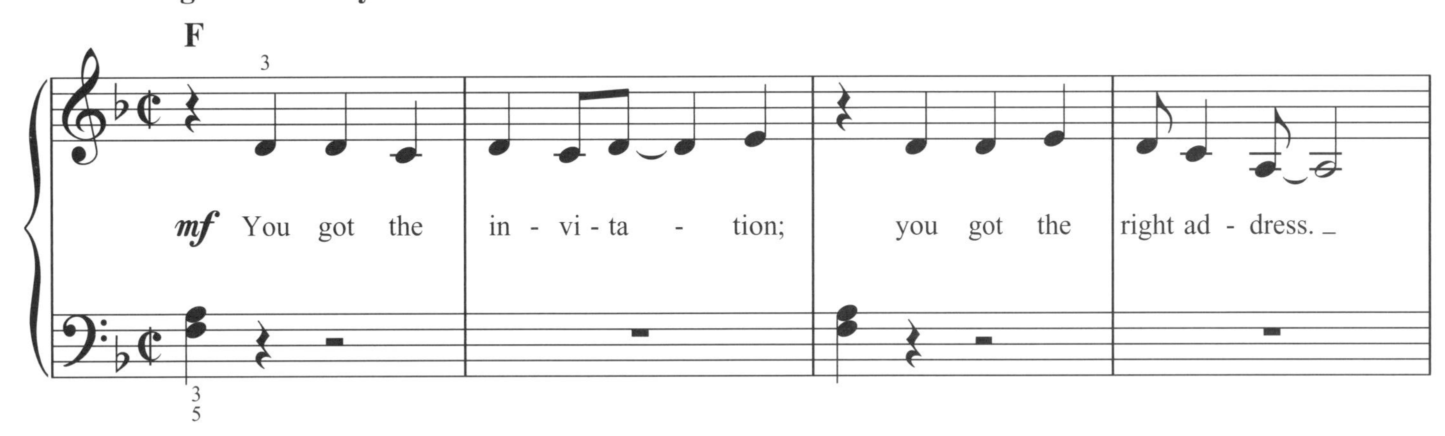

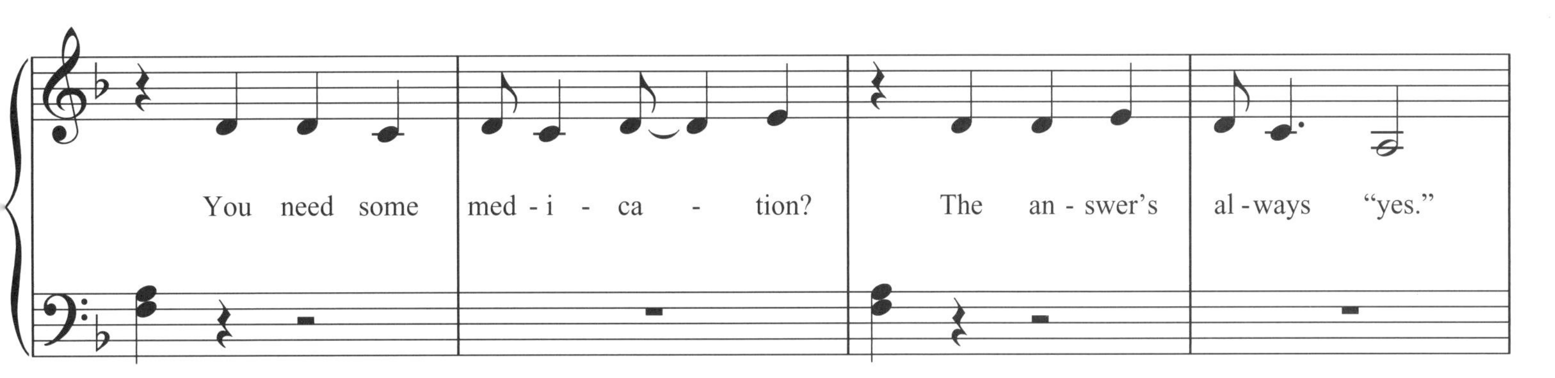

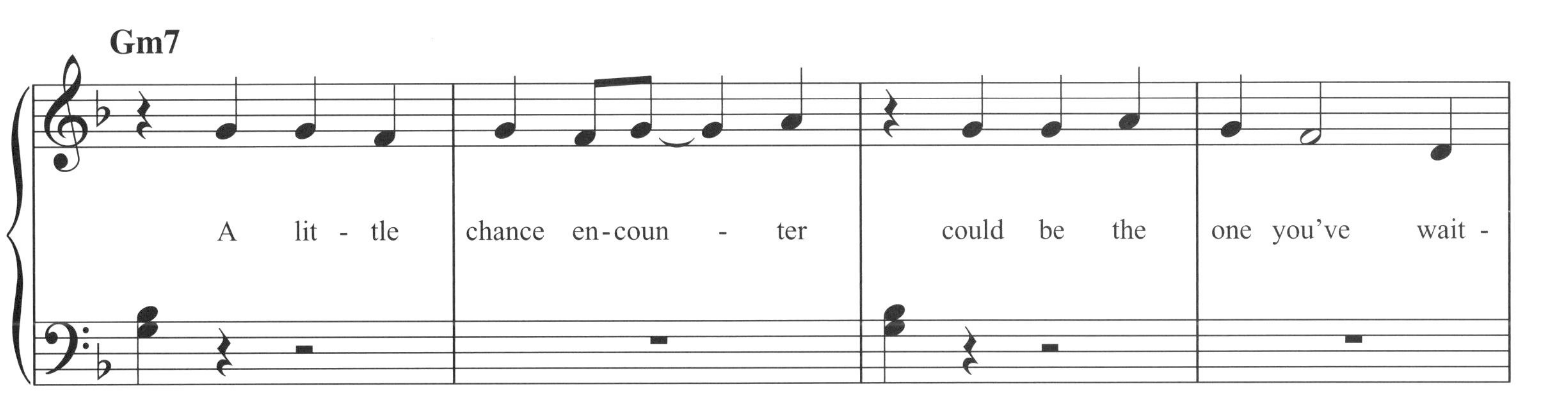

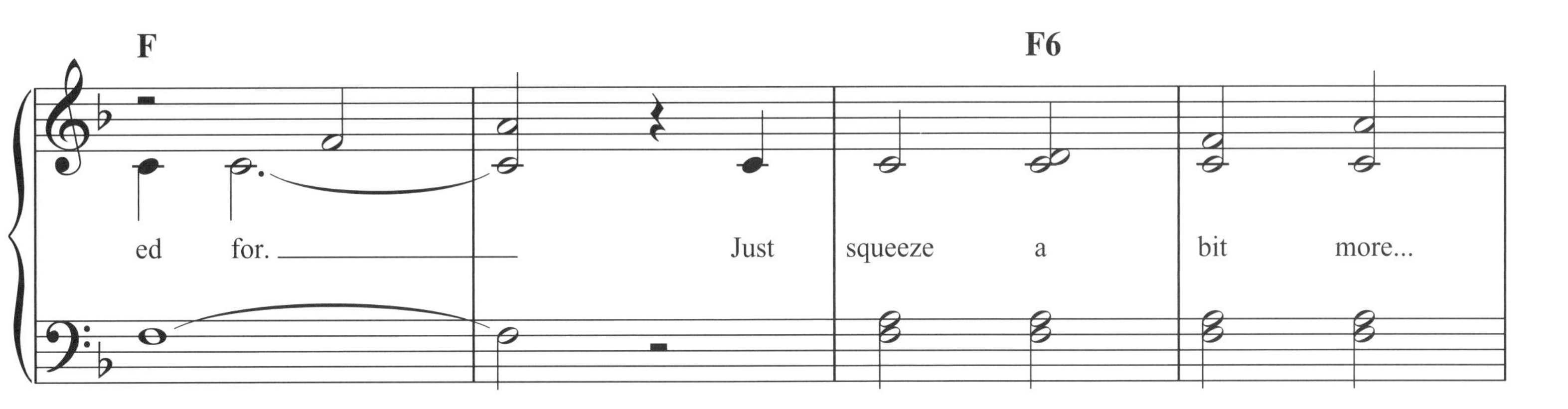

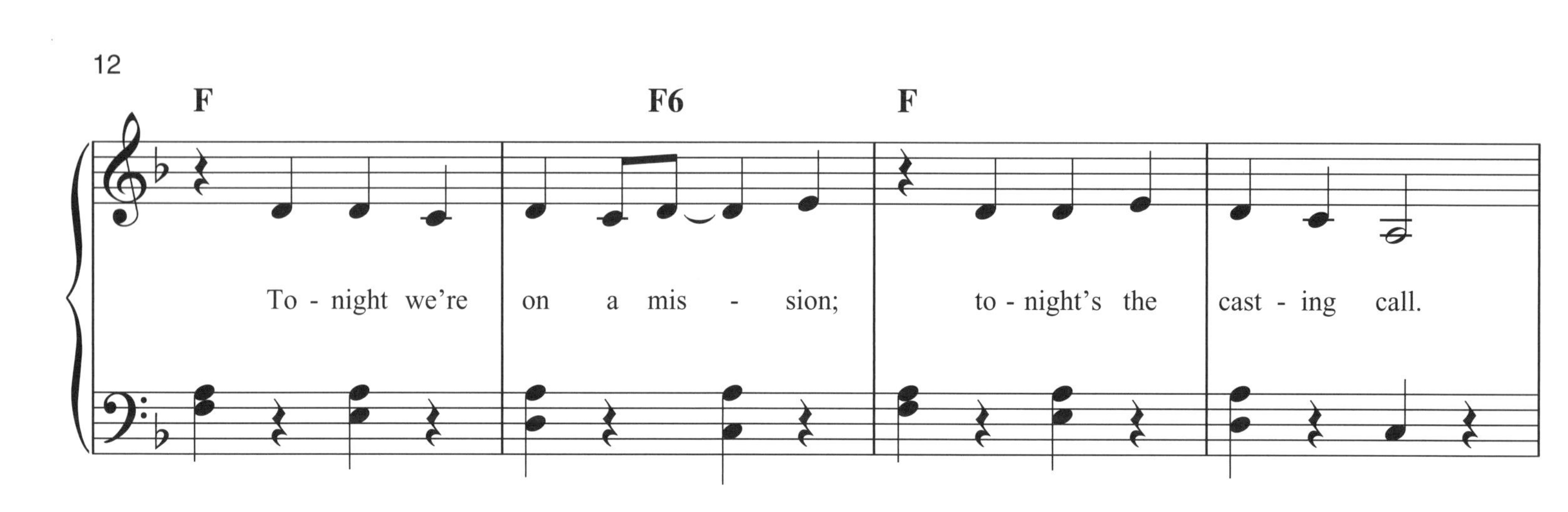
F
F6
F
To - night we're on a mis - sion; to - night's the cast - ing call.

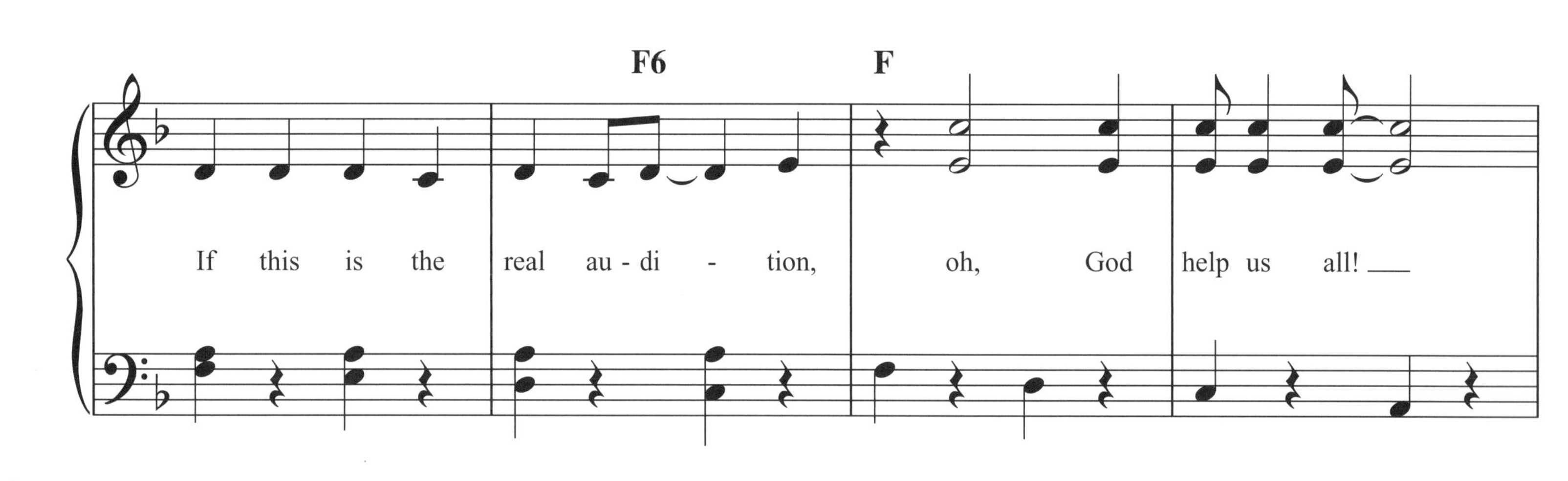
F6
F
If this is the real au - di - tion, oh, God help us all!

Gm7
You make the right im - pres - sion, then ev - 'ry - bod - y knows your

F
F6
name. We're in the fast lane!

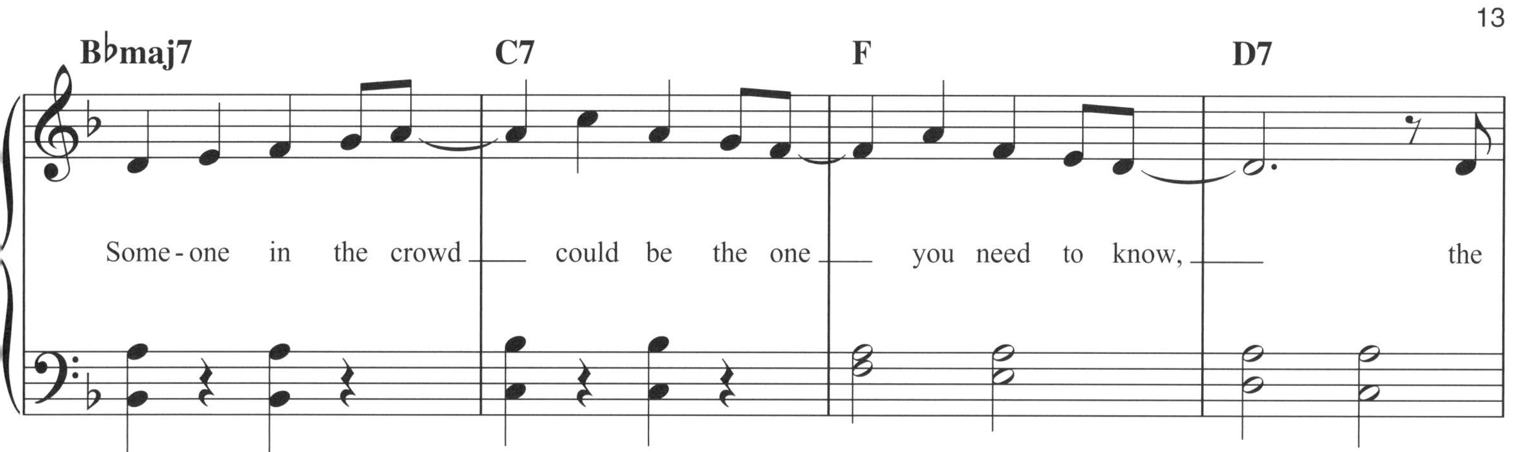
B♭maj7
C7
F
D7
Some - one in the crowd could be the one you need to know, the

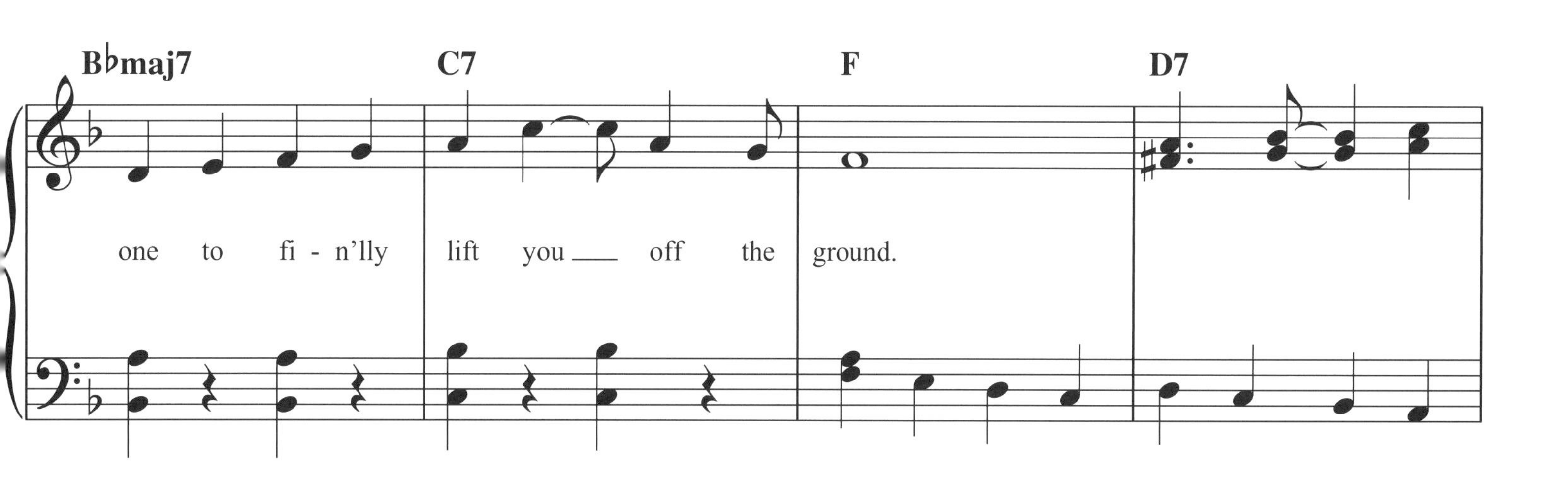
B♭maj7
C7
F
D7
one to fi - n'lly lift you off the ground.

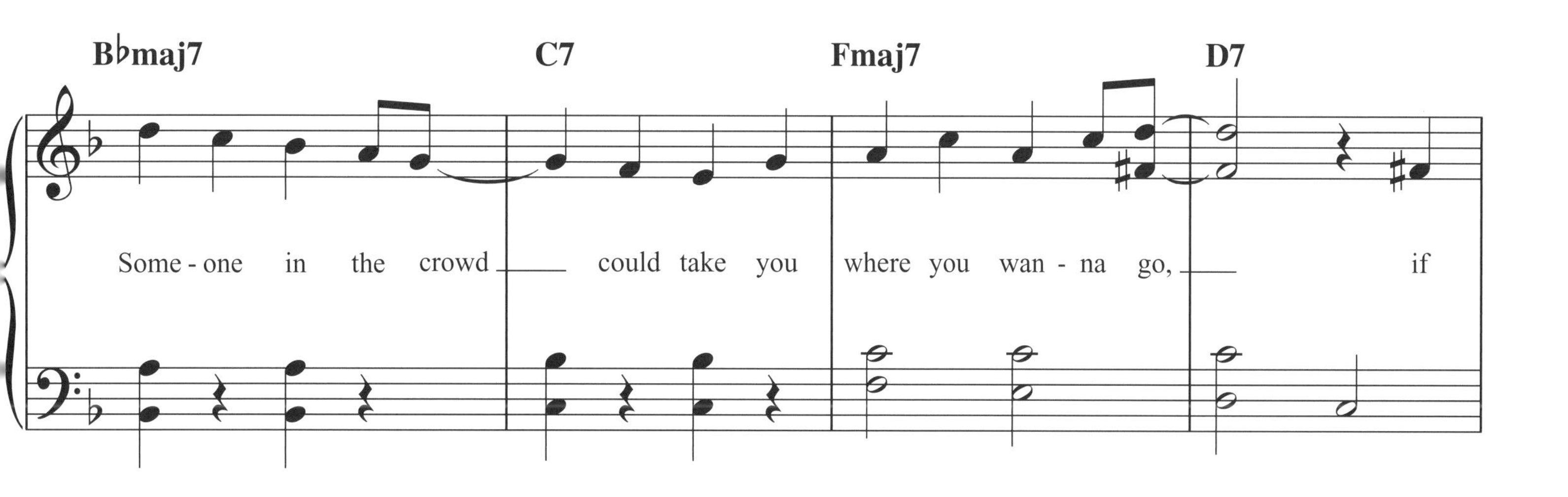
B♭maj7
C7
Fmaj7
D7
Some - one in the crowd could take you where you wan - na go, if

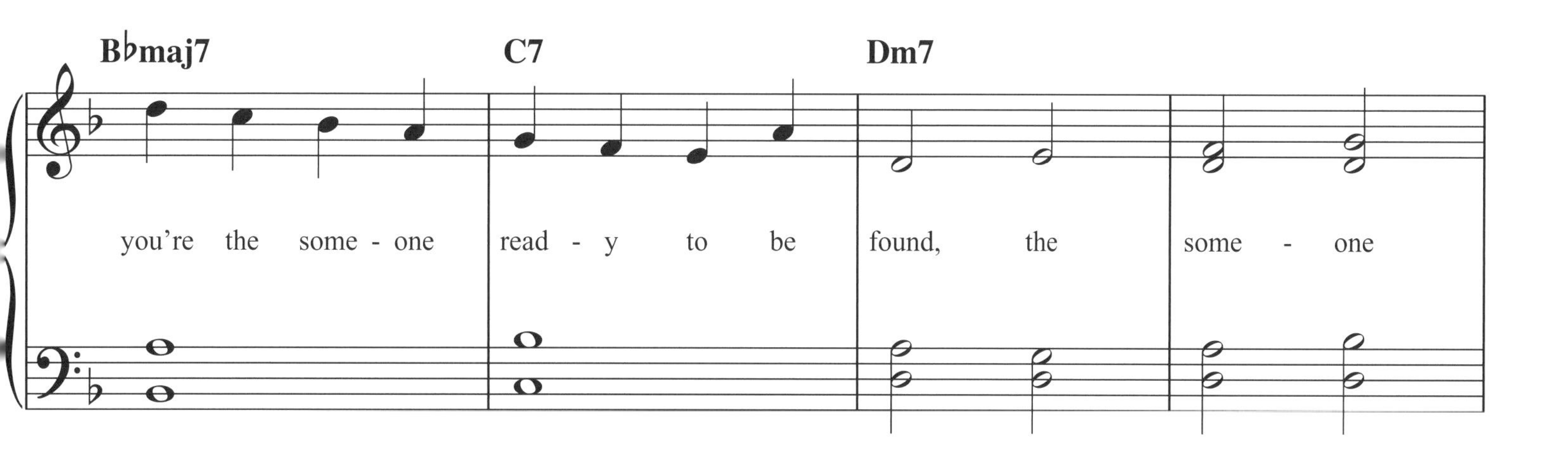
B♭maj7
C7
Dm7
you're the some - one read - y to be found, the some - one

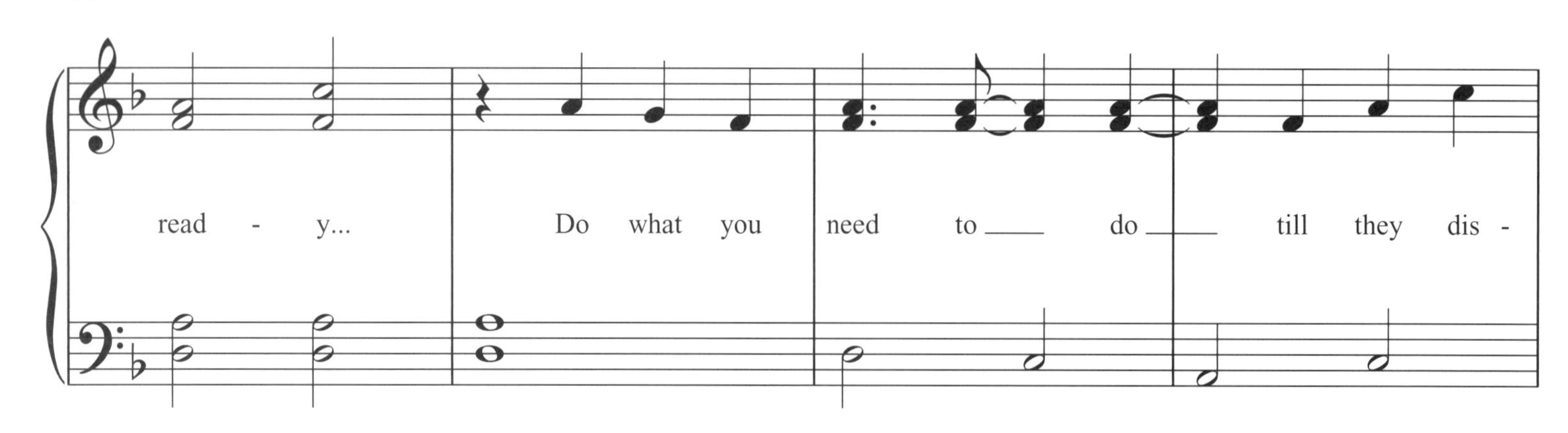
read - y...
Do what you
need to do till they dis -

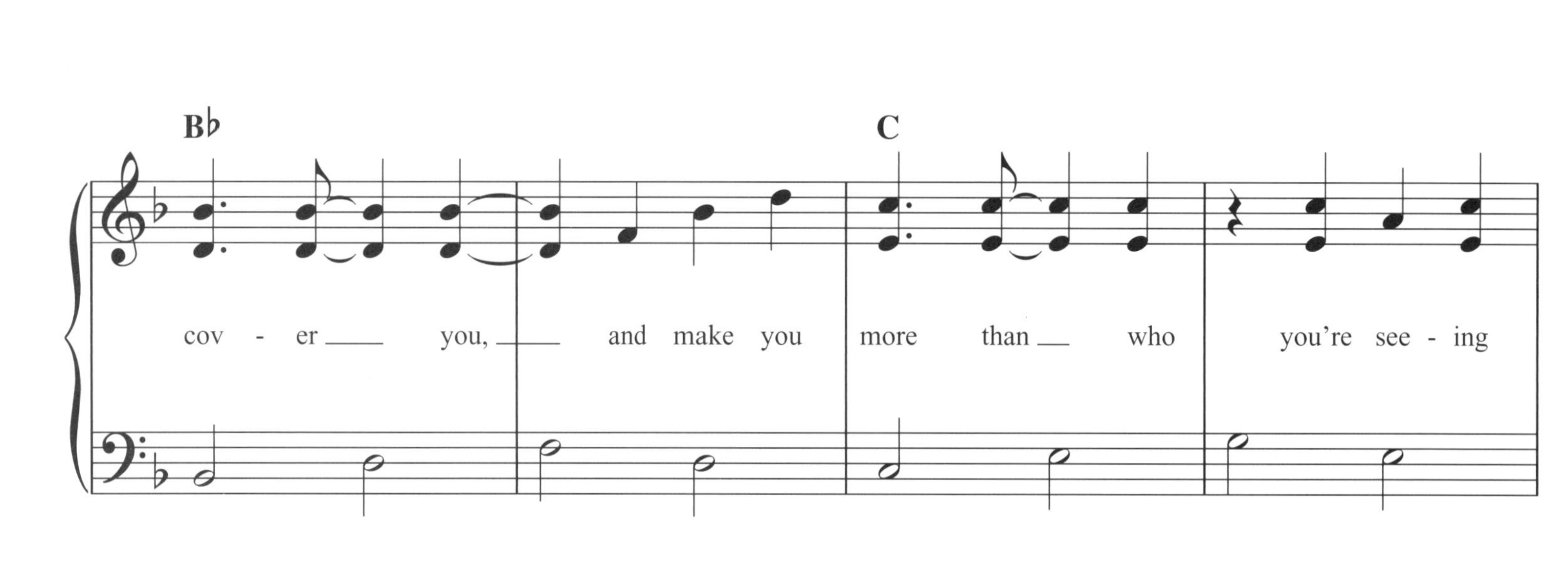
B♭
C
cov - er you, and make you
more than who
you're see - ing

F6
A7/C♯
Dm
now.
So with the
stars a - ligned,
I think I'll

B♭
C7
stay be - hind.
You've got to
go and find...

N.C.
(Spoken): that
some - one in the crowd.
p sub.

F6

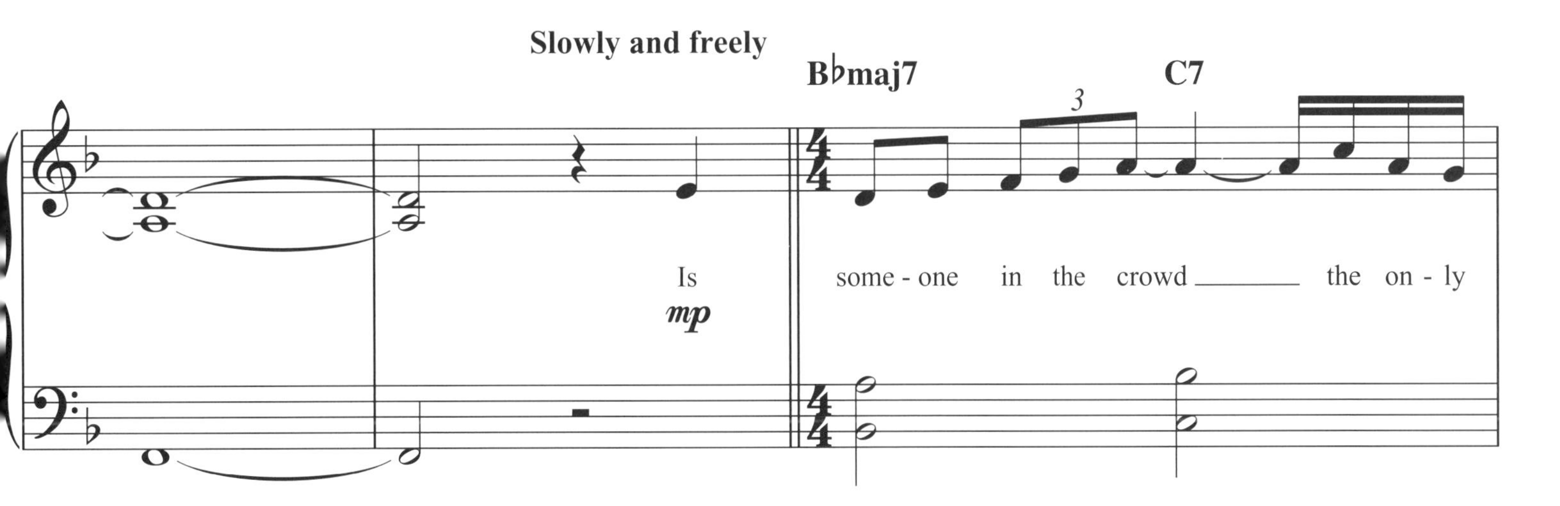
Slowly and freely
B♭maj7
C7
3
Is
mp
some - one in the crowd the on - ly

F
D7
B♭maj7
C7
Fmaj7
D7
3
thing you real - ly see,
watch - ing while the world keeps spin - ning 'round?

B♭maj7
C7
F
D7
B♭maj7
C7
3
3
Some-where there's a place _ where I find who I'm _ gon-na be, a some-where that's just wait-ing to be

Very slowly, in time
Dm(add2)
B♭maj7
C7
found.
p

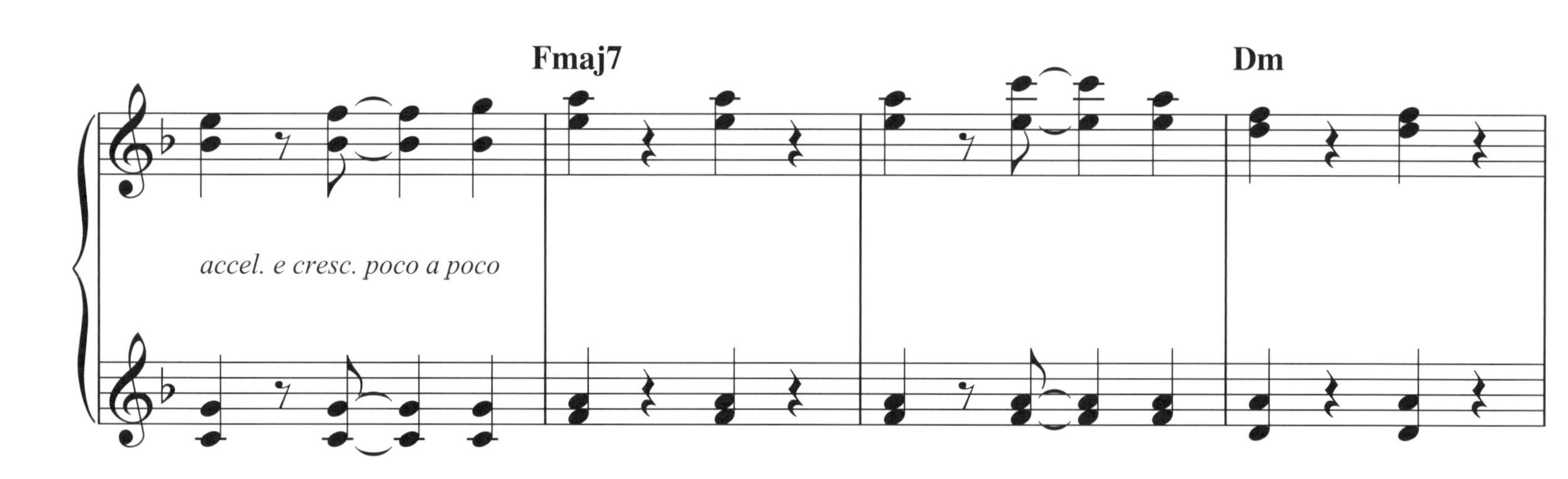
Fmaj7
Dm
accel. e cresc. poco a poco

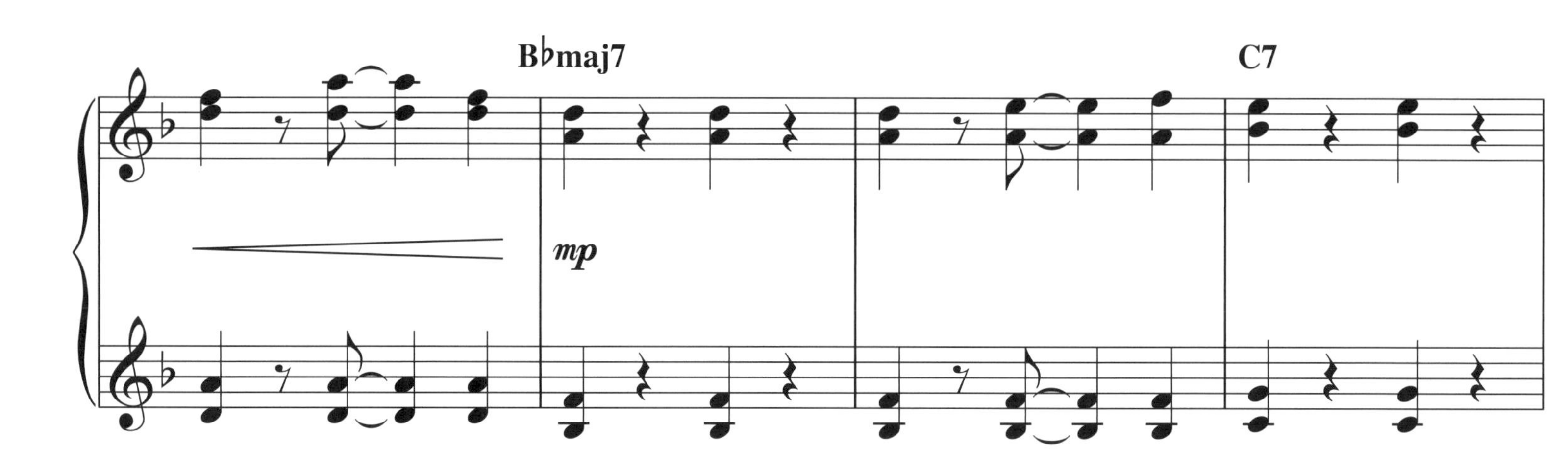
B♭maj7
C7
mp

Dm

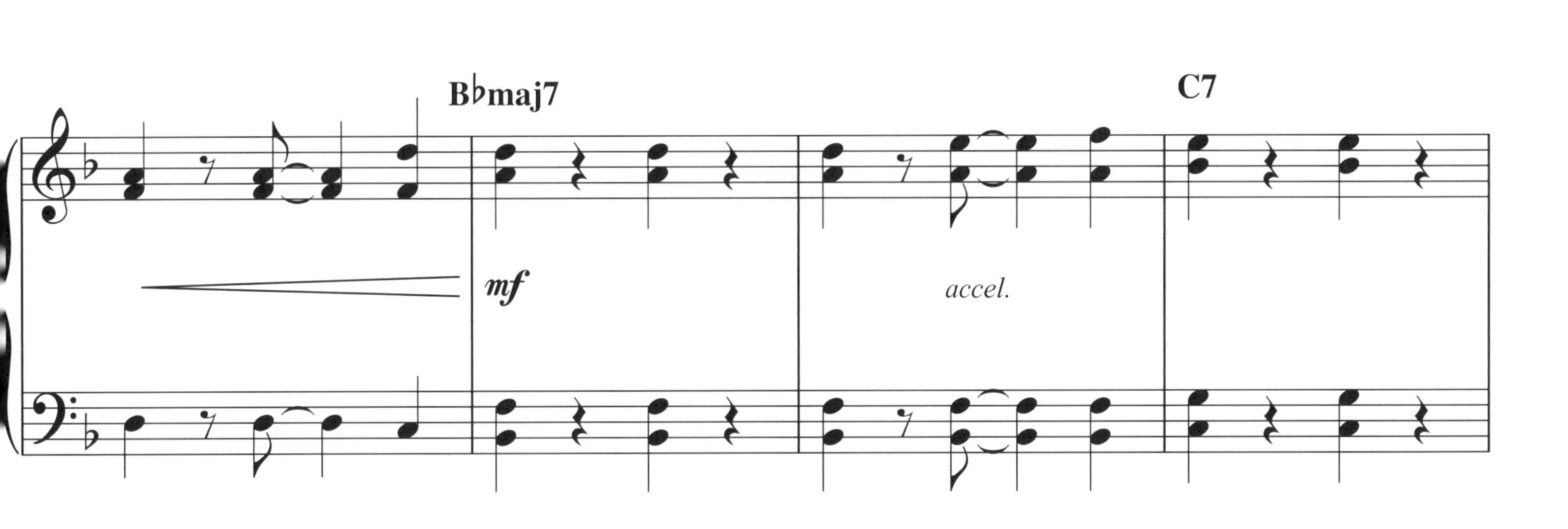
B♭maj7
C7
mf
accel.

Fmaj7
Dm

Em7
A7

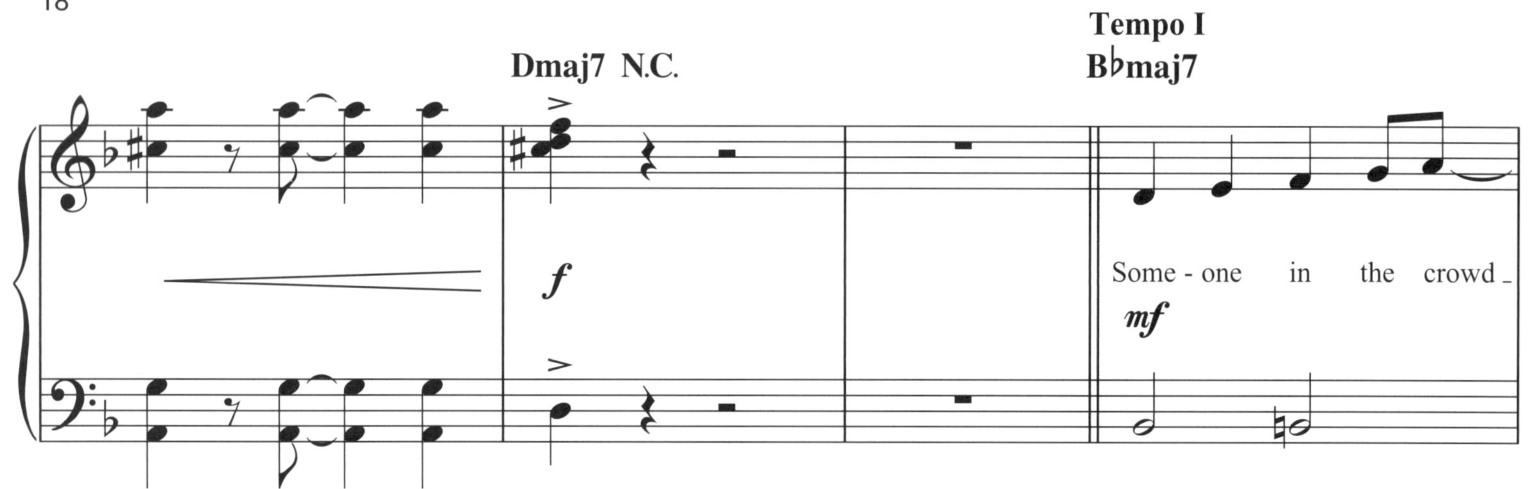
Dmaj7 N.C.
Tempo I
B♭maj7
f
Some - one in the crowd
mf

C
F
D7
B♭maj7
could be the one you need to know, the some - one who could lift

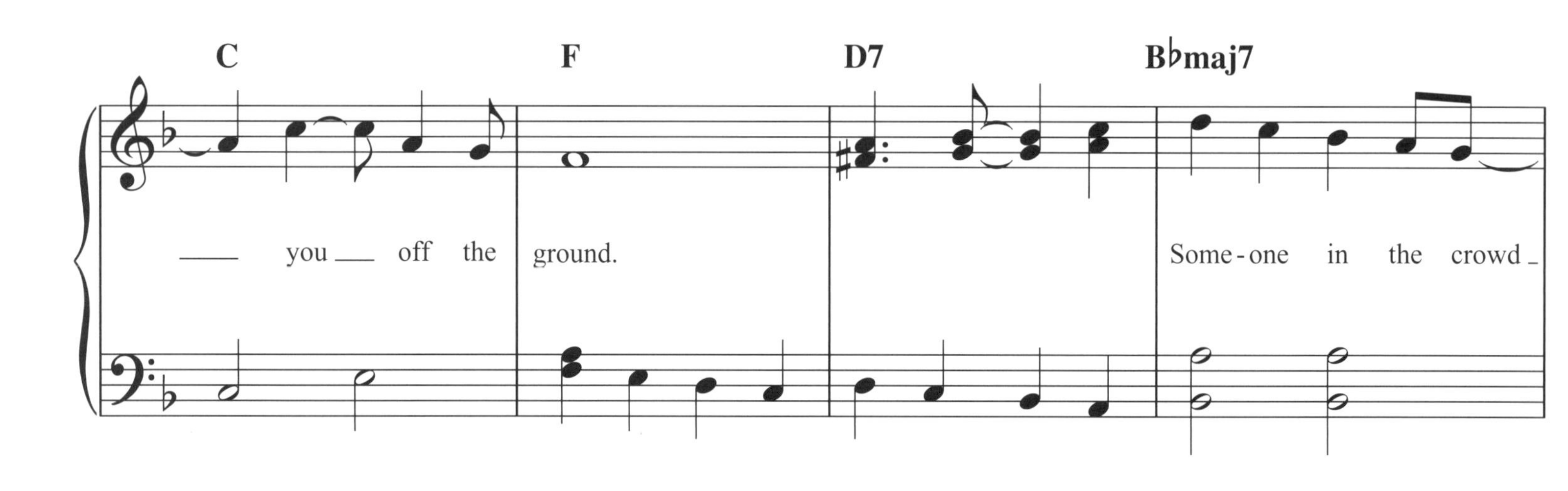
C
F
D7
B♭maj7
you off the ground. Some - one in the crowd

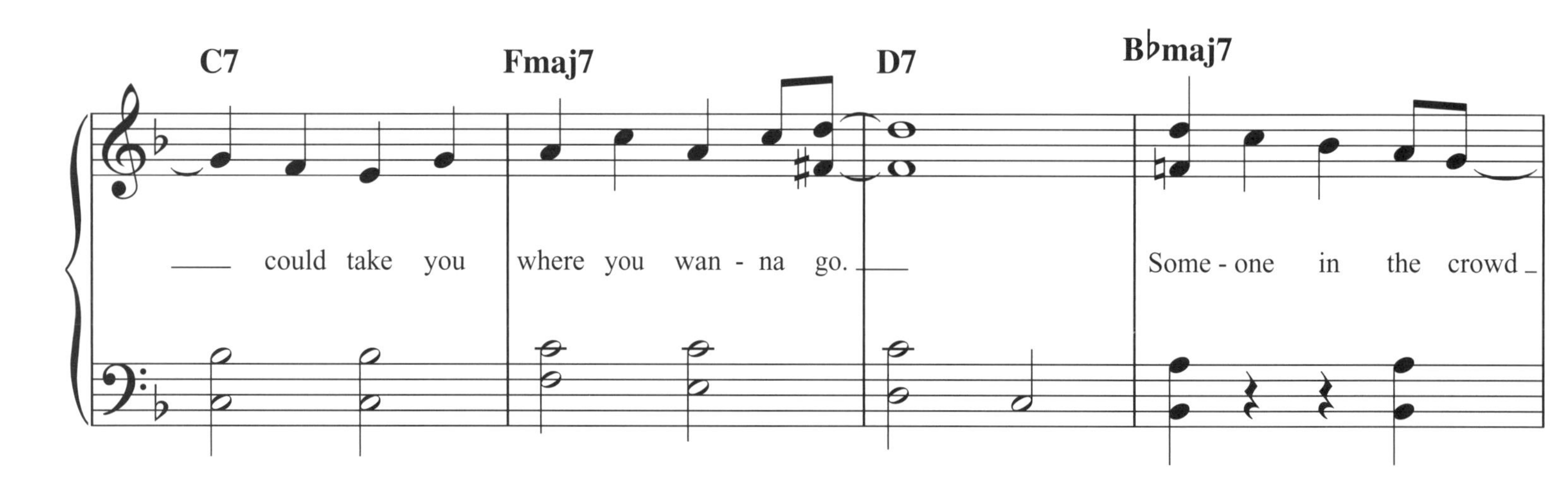
C7
Fmaj7
D7
B♭maj7
could take you where you wan - na go. Some - one in the crowd

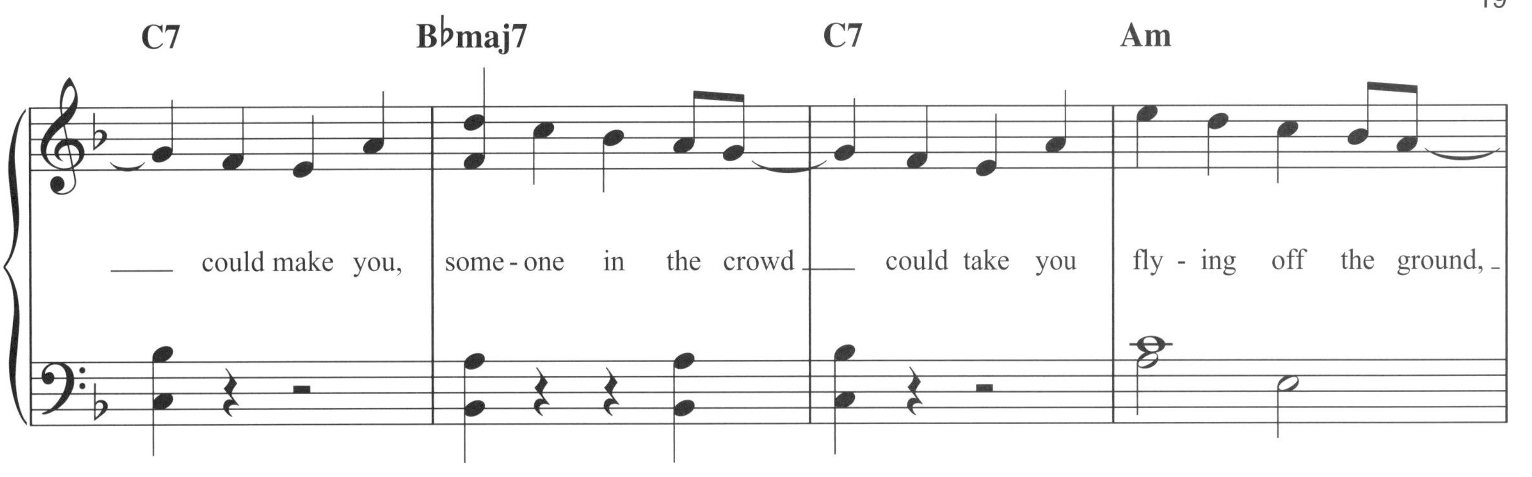
C7
B♭maj7
C7
Am
could make you, some - one in the crowd could take you fly - ing off the ground,

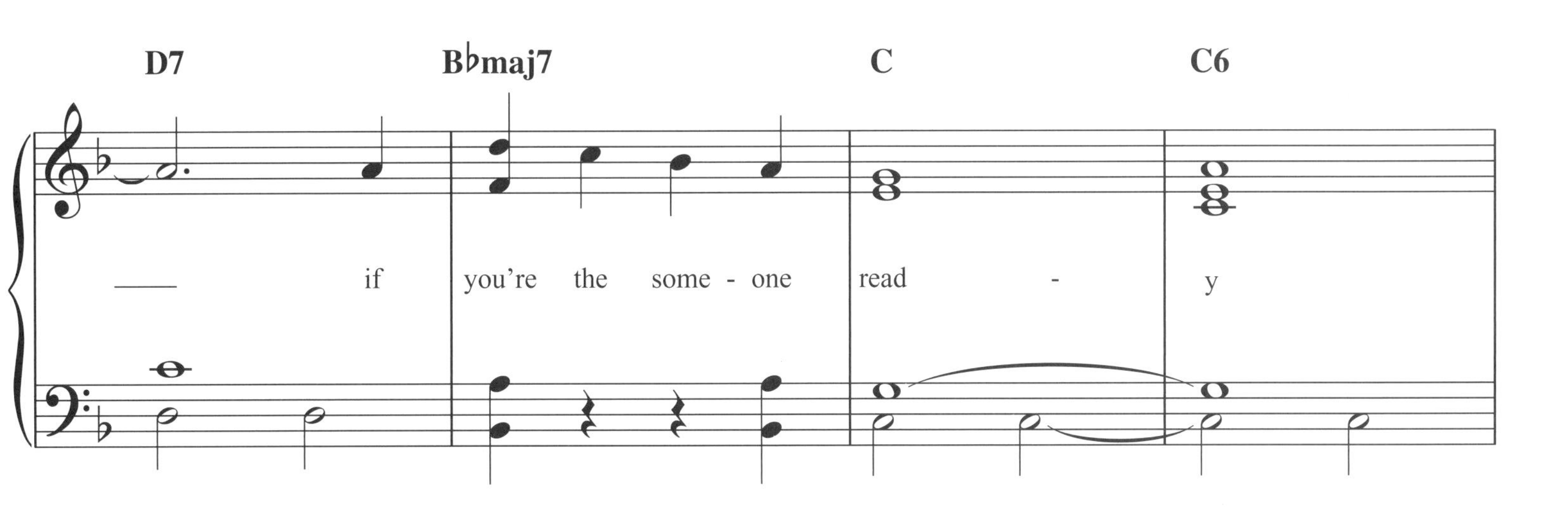
D7
B♭maj7
C
C6
if you're the some - one read - y

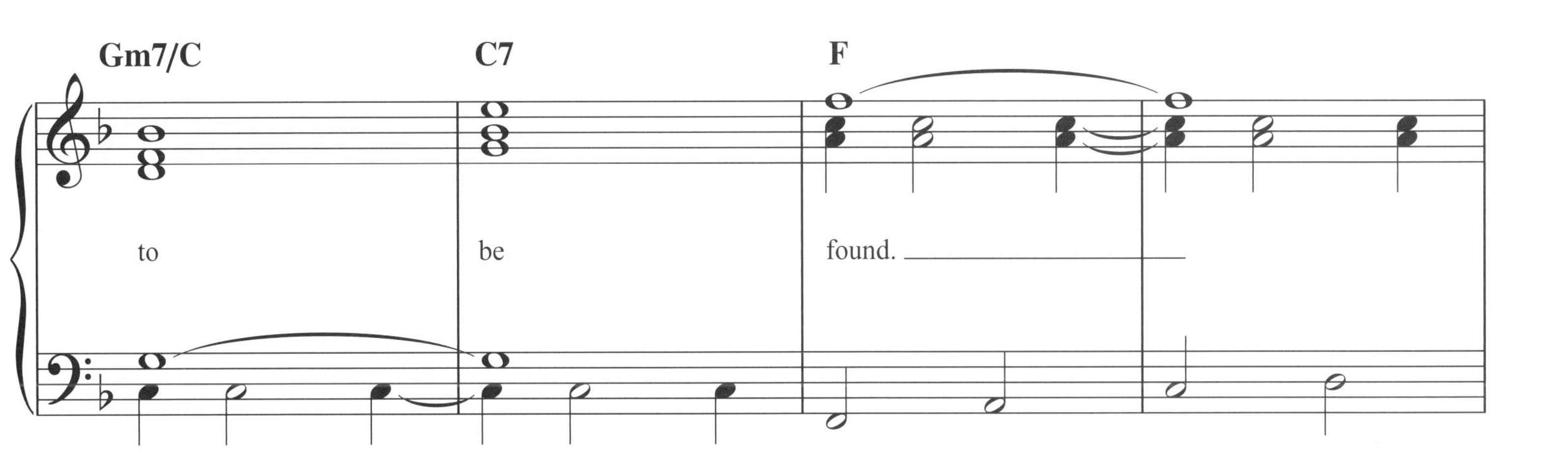
Gm7/C
C7
F
to be found.

F6
F

MIA & SEBASTIAN'S THEME

Music by
JUSTIN HURWITZ

Moderately slow, expressively

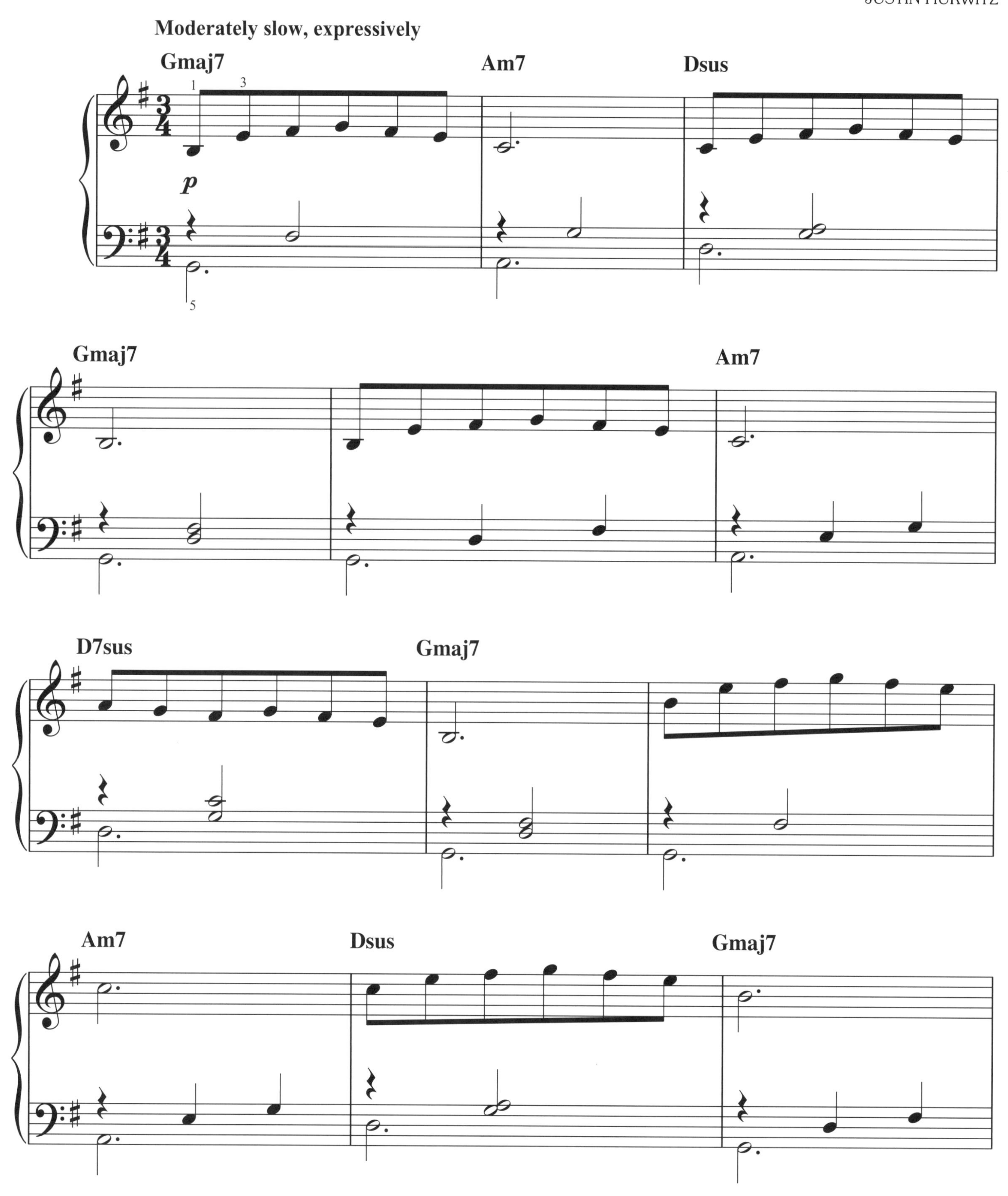

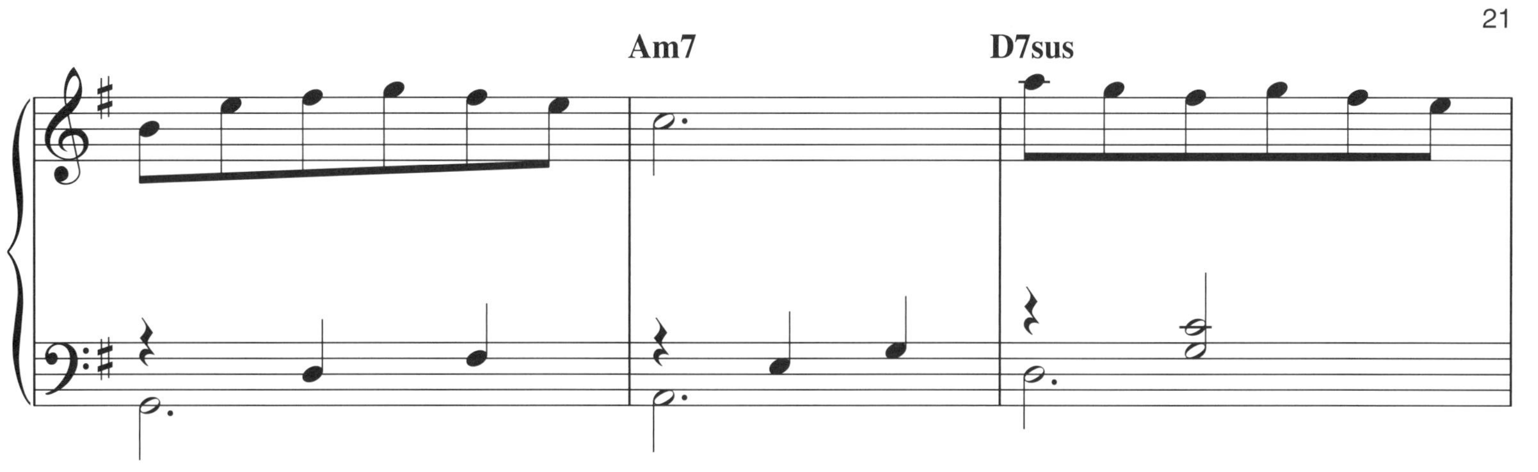
Am7
D7sus

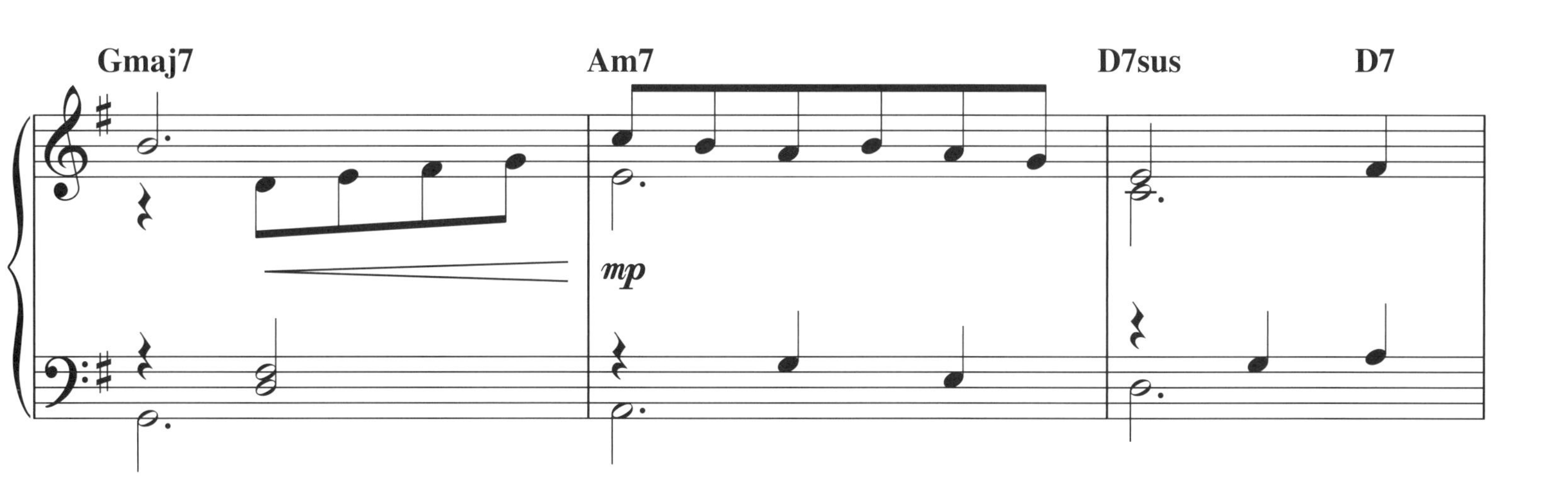
Gmaj7
Am7
D7sus
D7
mp

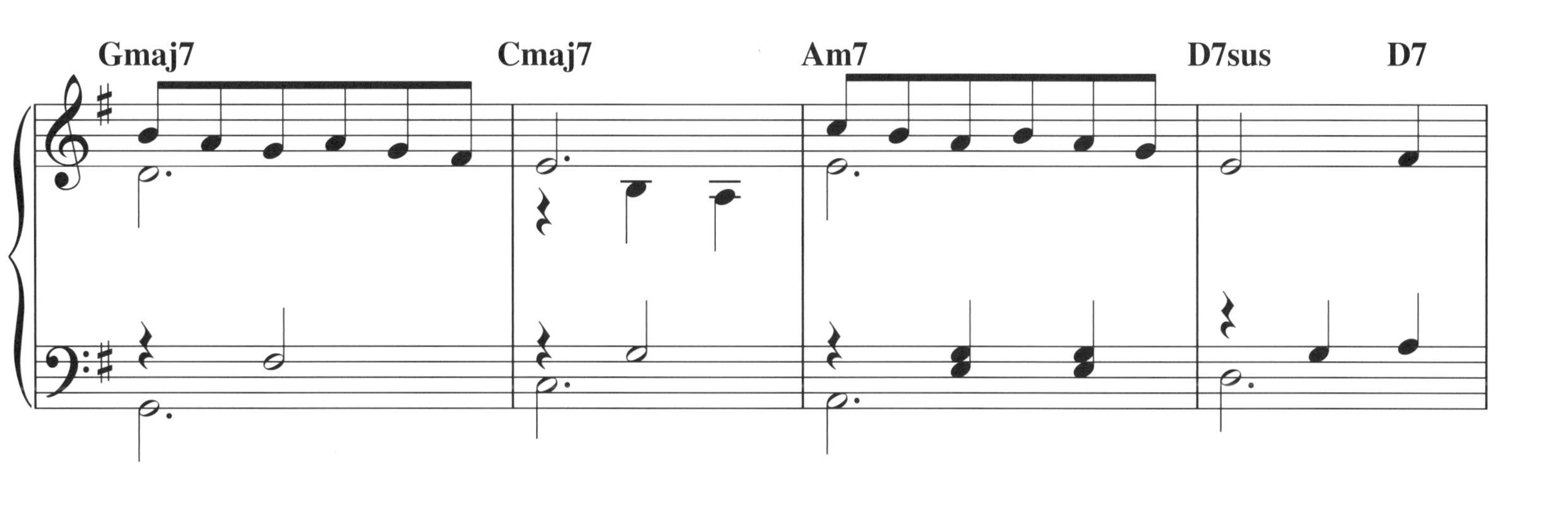
Gmaj7
Cmaj7
Am7
D7sus
D7

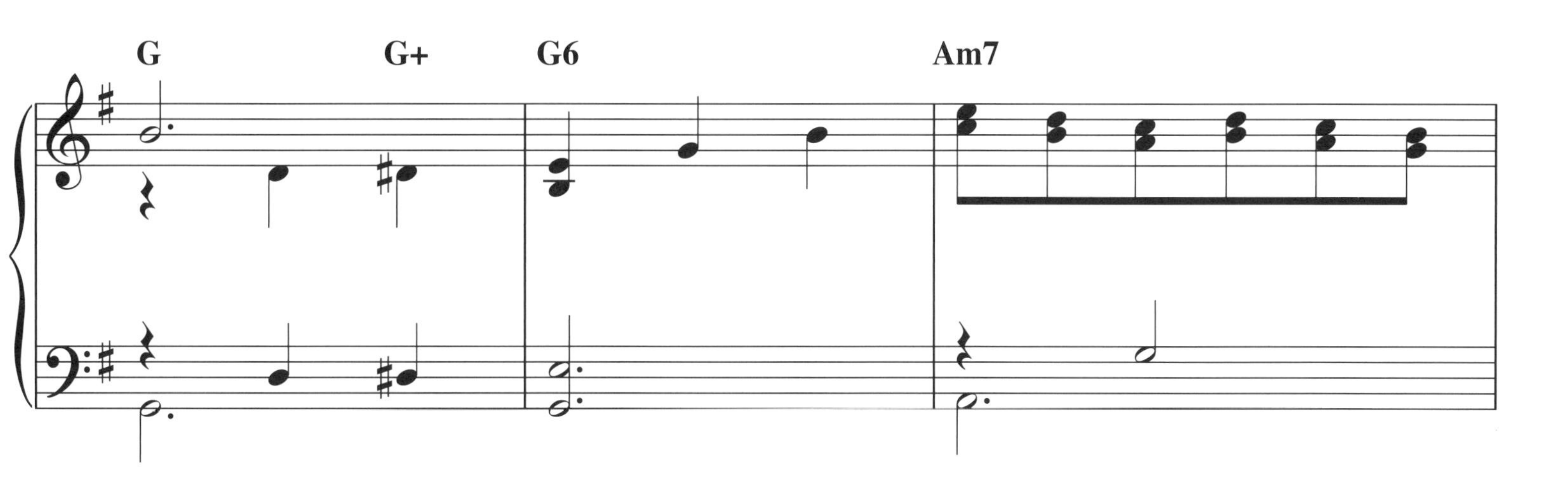
G
G+
G6
Am7

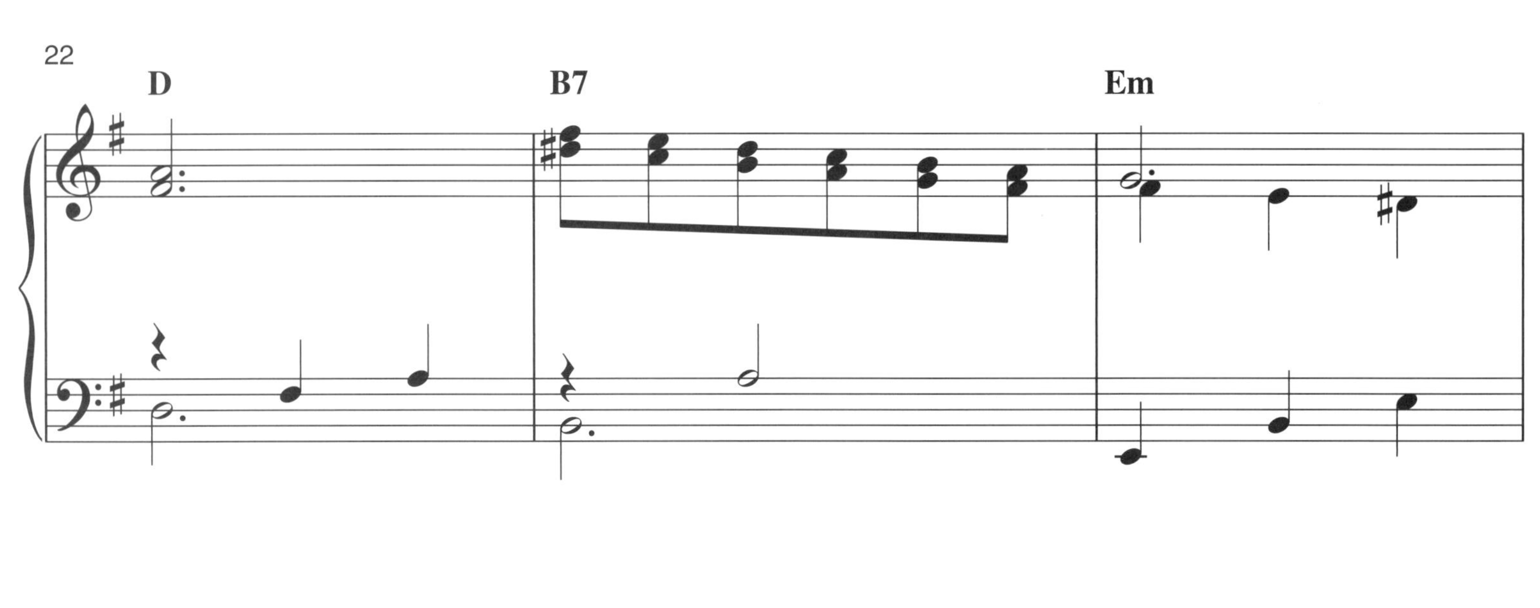
D
B7
Em

C
Em/B
B♭7
A7♭5
cresc. e accel.

D7♭5
C♯7
C13
accel.
rit.

As fast as possible, freely
B7♯9

Fm/E
f
A7#9
D7#9
8va
3
3
(8va)
G7#5
rit.
Fast
Cm

A LOVELY NIGHT

Music by JUSTIN HURWITZ
Lyrics by BENJ PASEK & JUSTIN PAUL

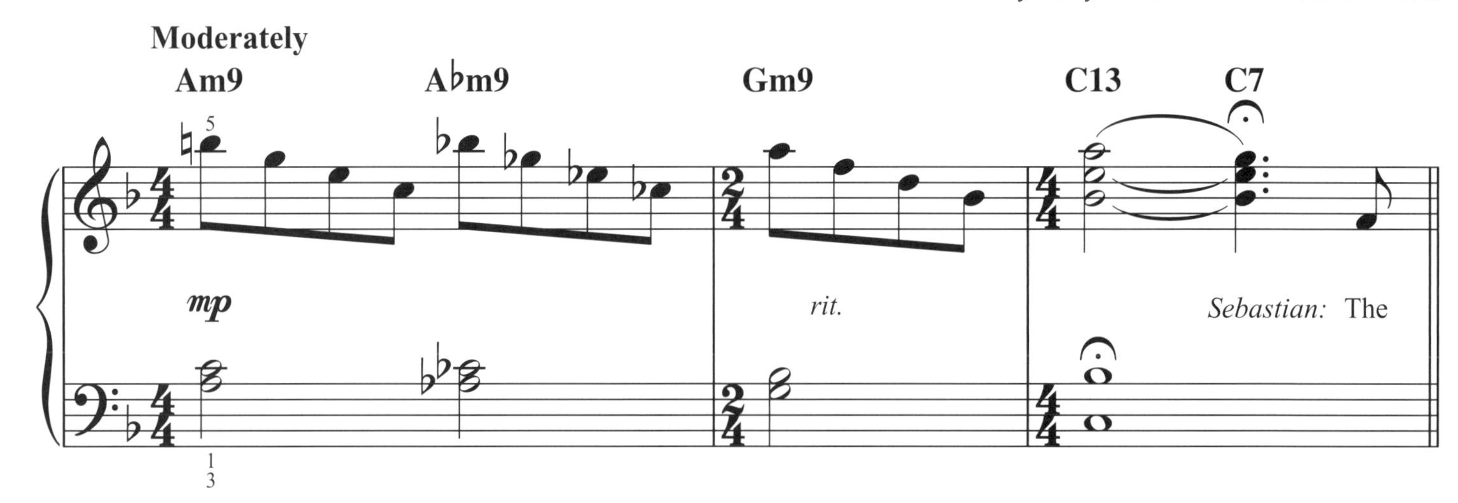

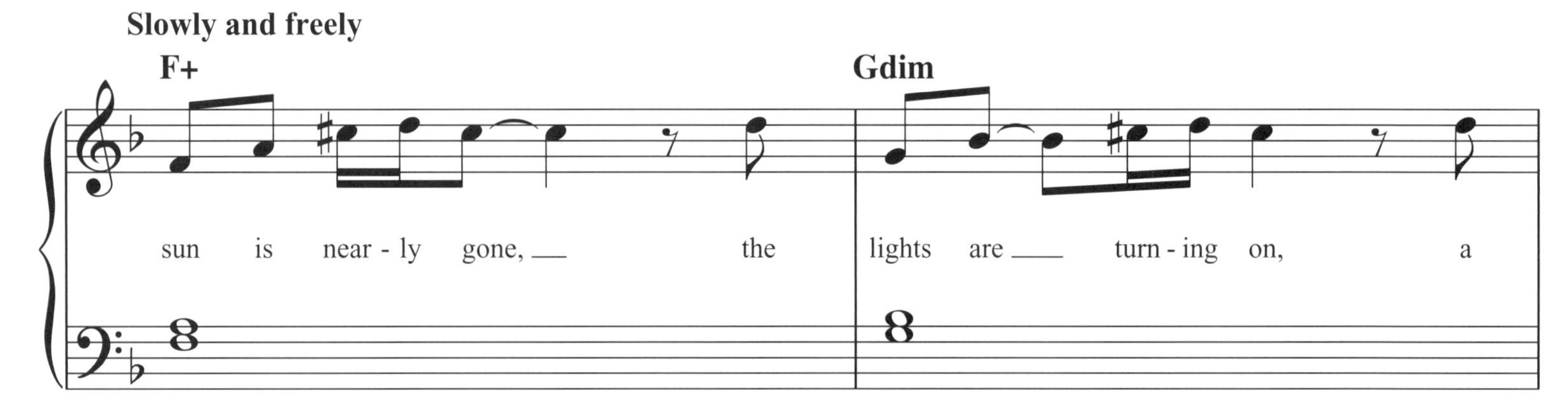

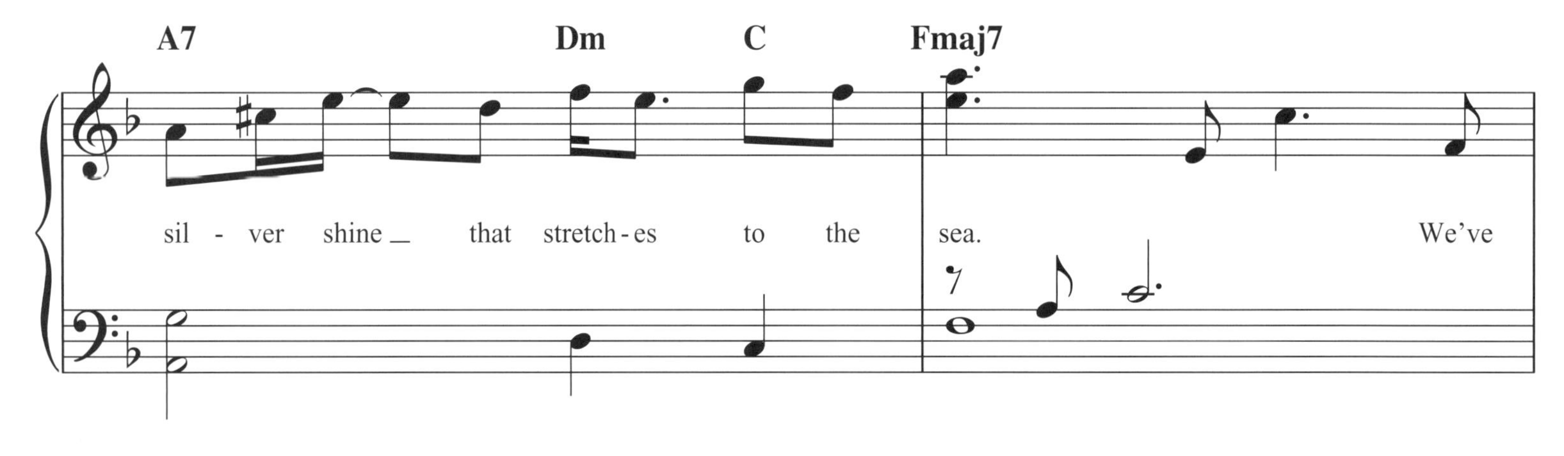

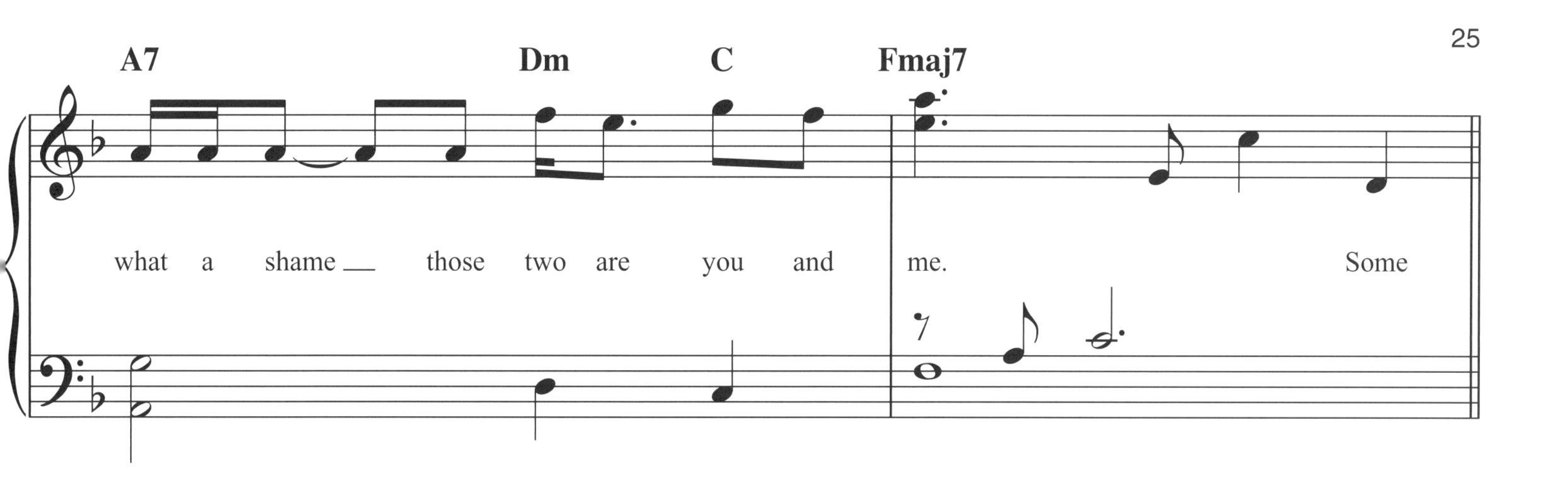
A7
Dm
C
Fmaj7
what a shame __ those two are you and me. Some

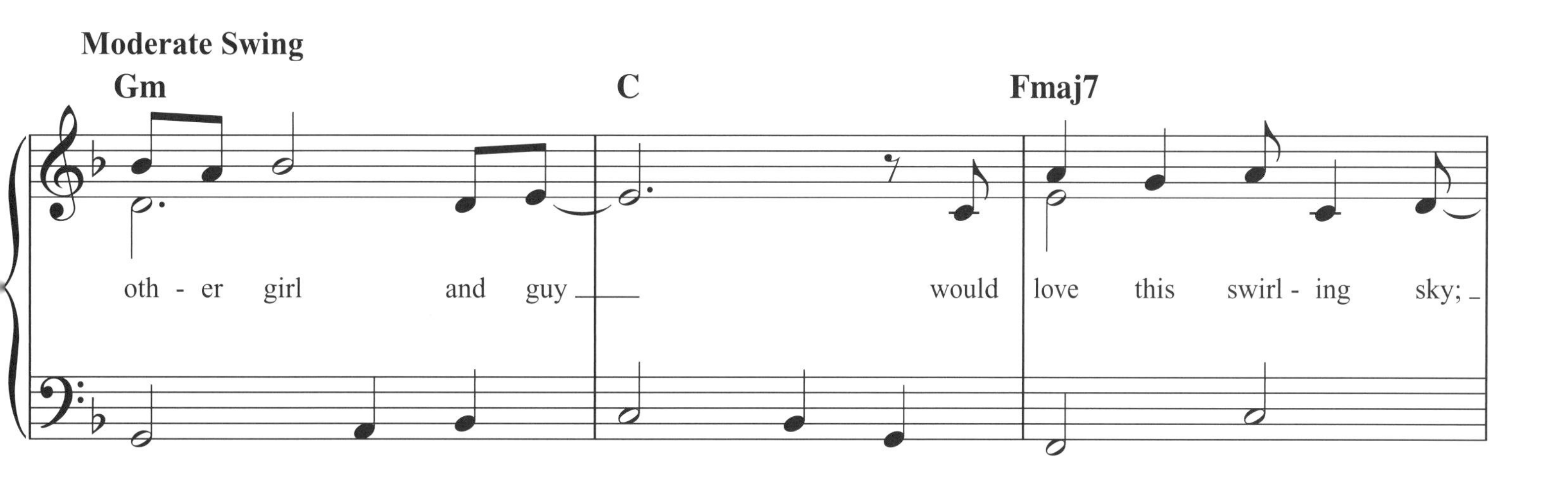
Moderate Swing
Gm
C
Fmaj7
oth - er girl and guy __ would love this swirl - ing sky; _

D
Gm
C
__ but there's on - ly you and I, __ and

Fmaj7
A
B♭maj7
we've got no shot. This could nev - er be; __

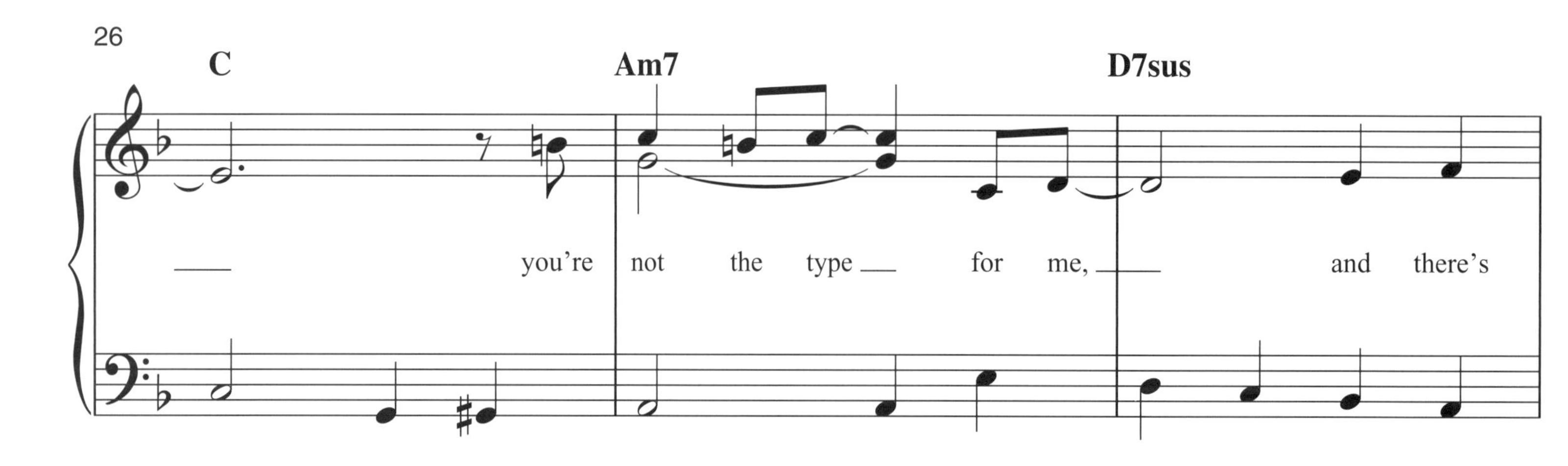
C
Am7
D7sus
you're not the type for me, and there's

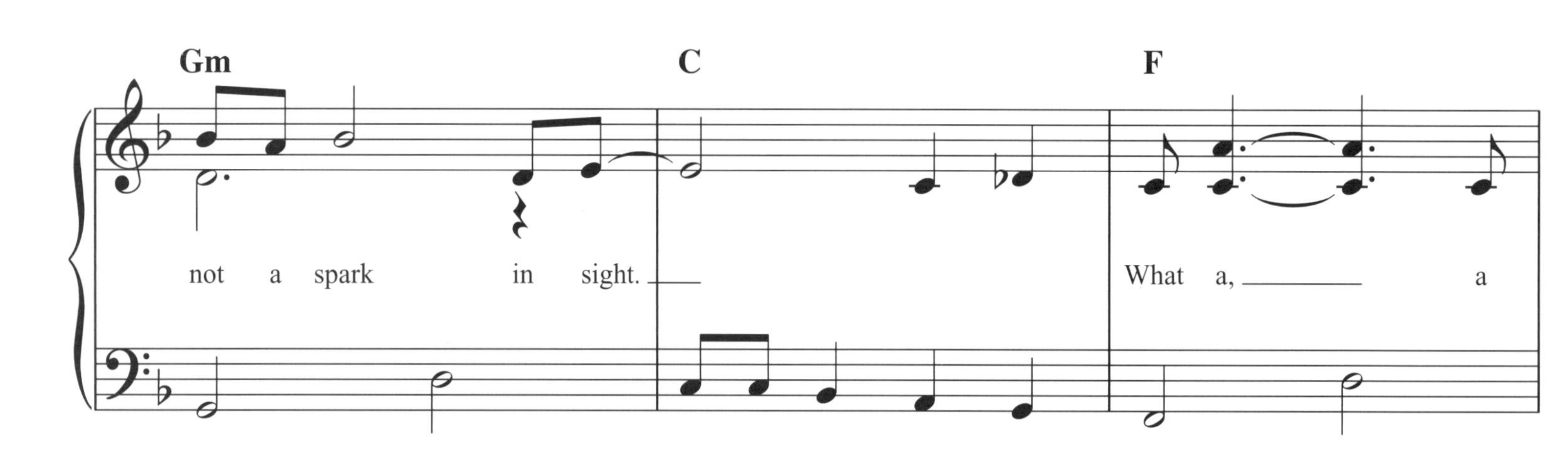
Gm
C
F
not a spark in sight.
What a, a

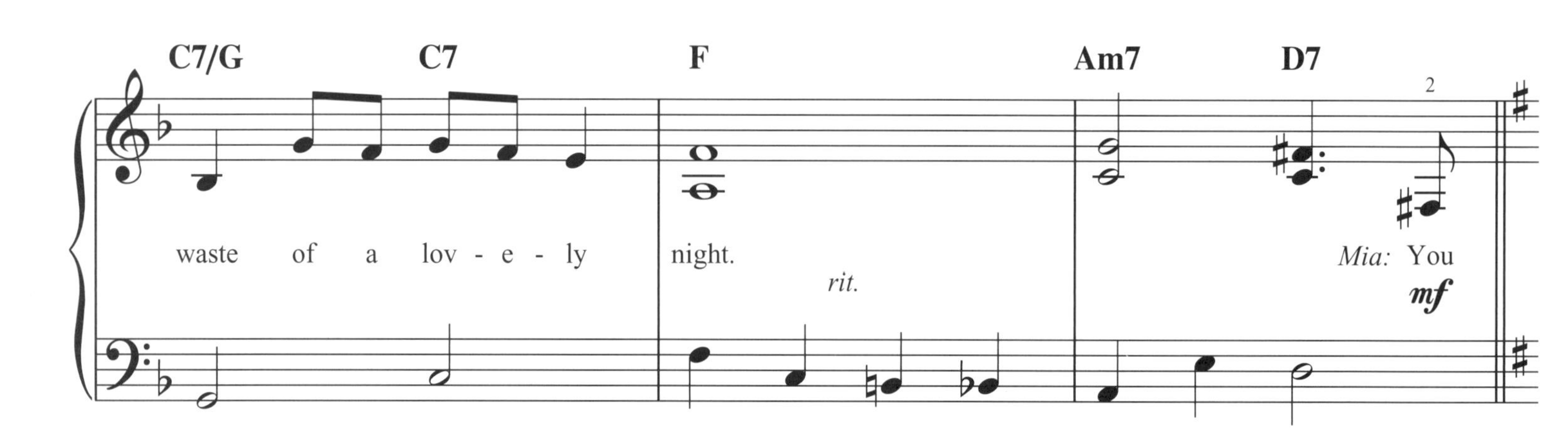
C7/G
C7
F
Am7
D7
waste of a lov - e - ly night.
rit.
Mia: You
mf

A bit faster
G+
Adim
say there's noth - ing here; well let's make some - thing clear: I

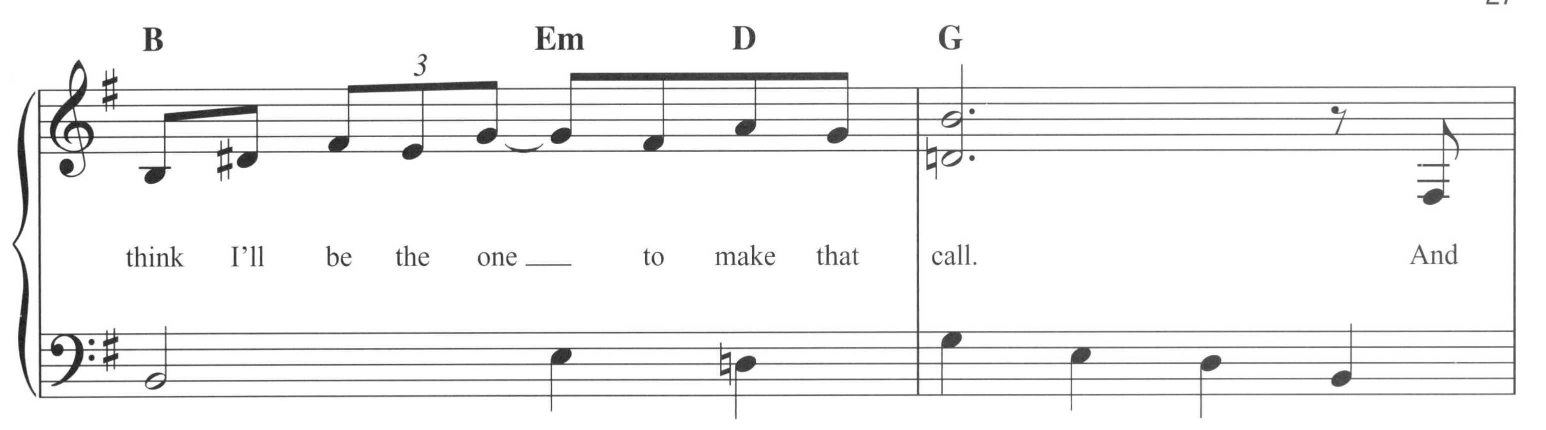
B
3
Em
D
G
think I'll be the one ___ to make that call. And

G+
Adim
though you look so cute in your po - ly - es - ter suit, you're

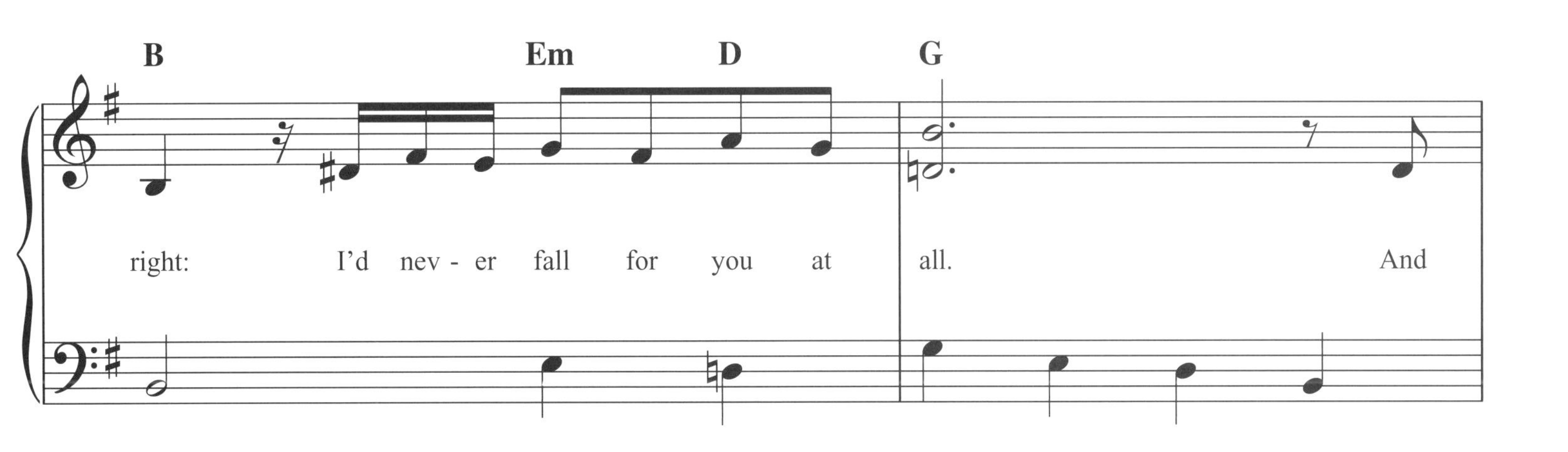
B
Em
D
G
right: I'd nev - er fall for you at all. And

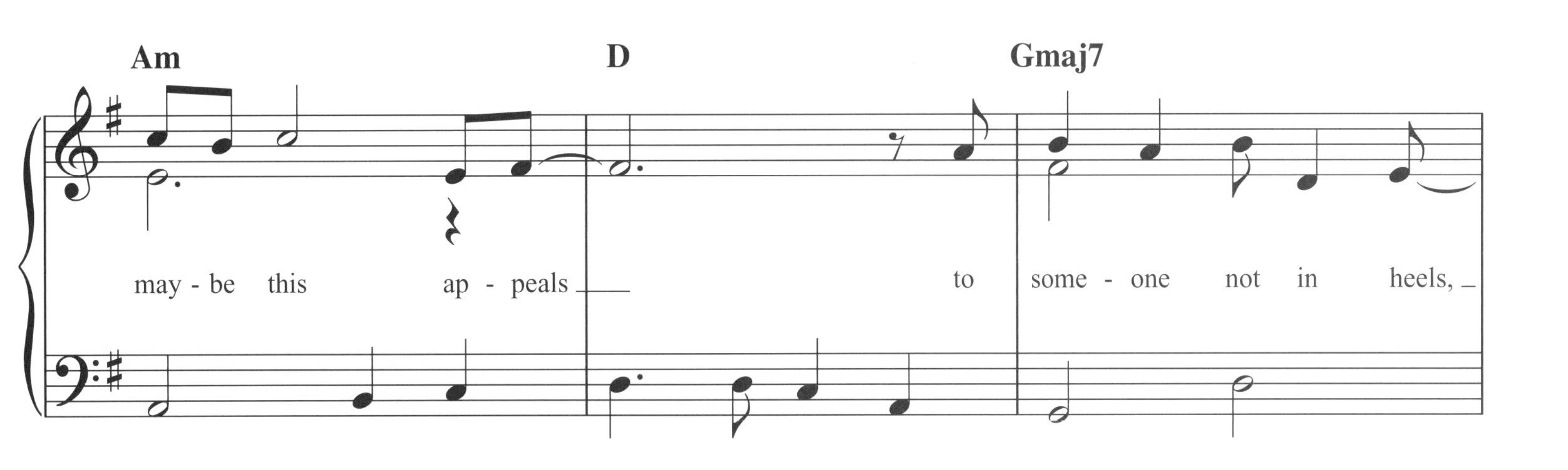
Am
D
Gmaj7
may - be this ap - peals ___ to some - one not in heels, ___

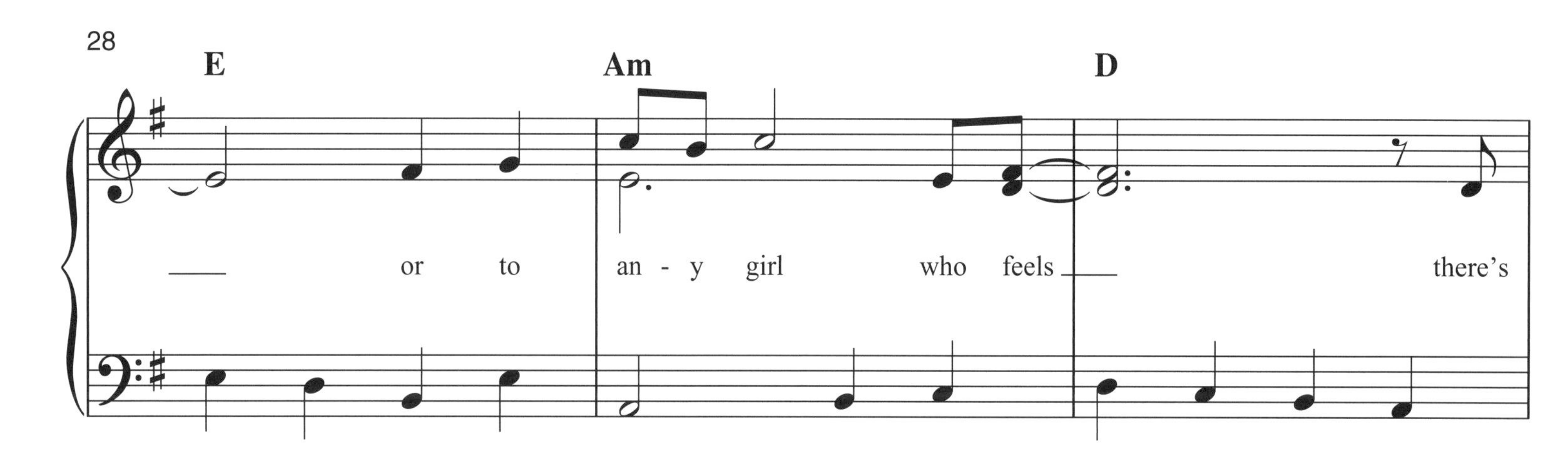
E
Am
D
or to
an - y girl who feels
there's

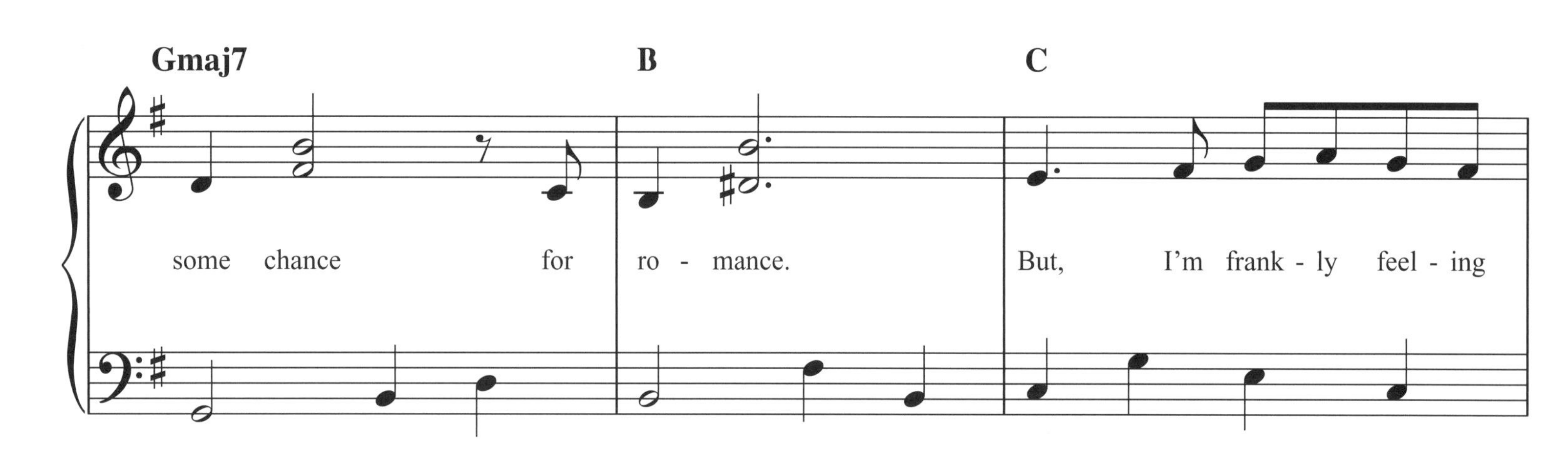
Gmaj7
B
C
some chance for
ro - mance.
But, I'm frank - ly feel - ing

D
Cmaj7
D
noth - ing.
Sebastian: Is that
Mia: Or it could be less than
so?
noth - ing.
Sebastian: Good to

C
D7
C
know! So you a -
Mia: That's right.
gree?
Both: What a waste of a

Faster
D
Am7
A♭dim7
G+/D
Adim/D
love - ly night!
rit.
Em/D
G/D
G+/D
Adim/D
Em/D
G/D
Am7
D7
Gmaj7

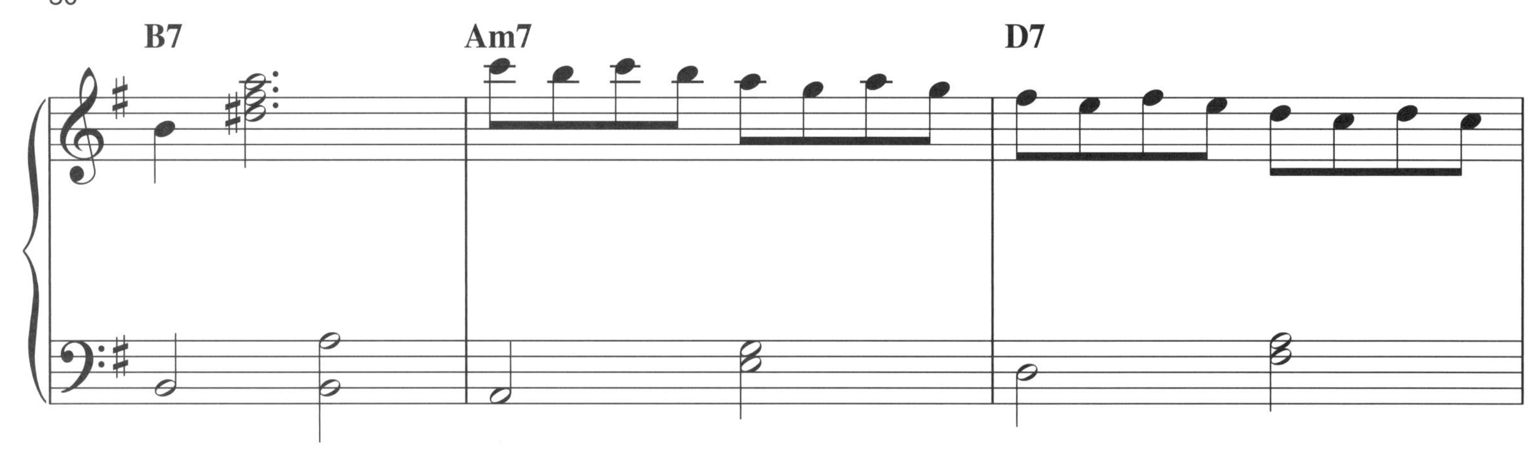
B7
Am7
D7

Gmaj7
B7
Am7

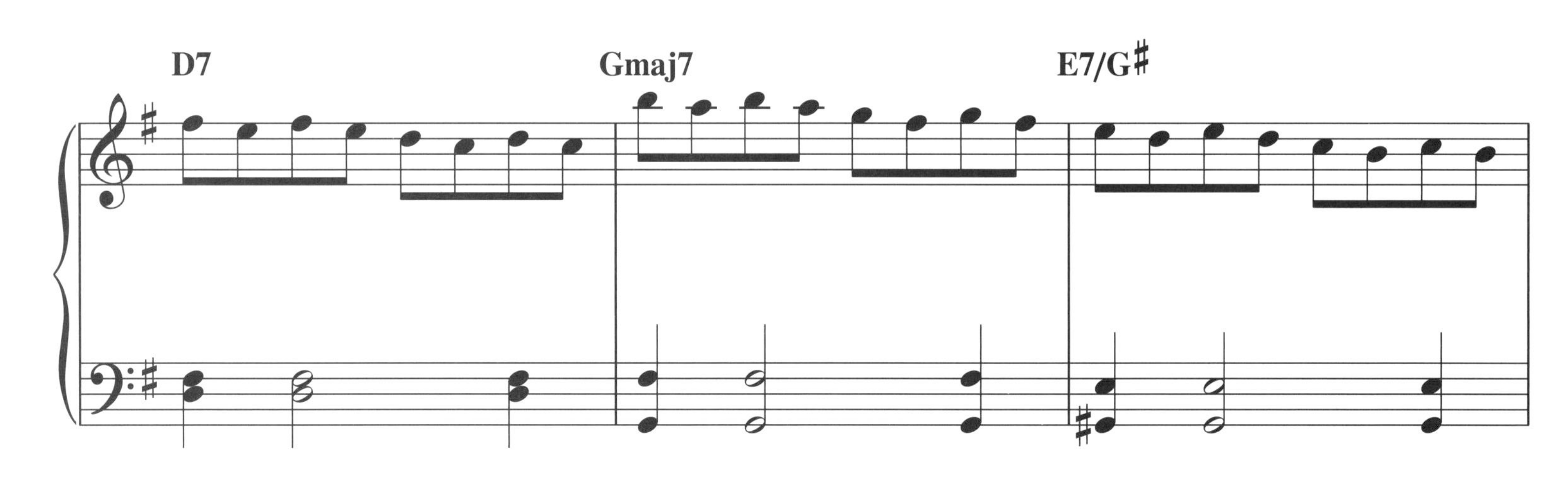
D7
Gmaj7
E7/G♯

Am7
D7
Gmaj7

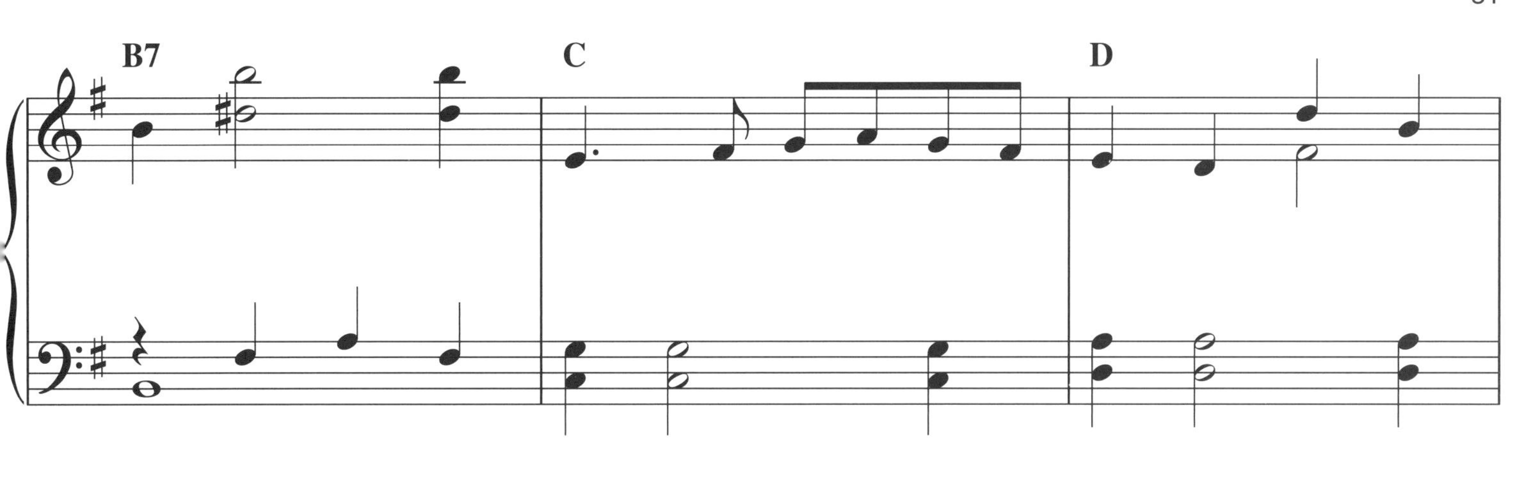
B7
C
D

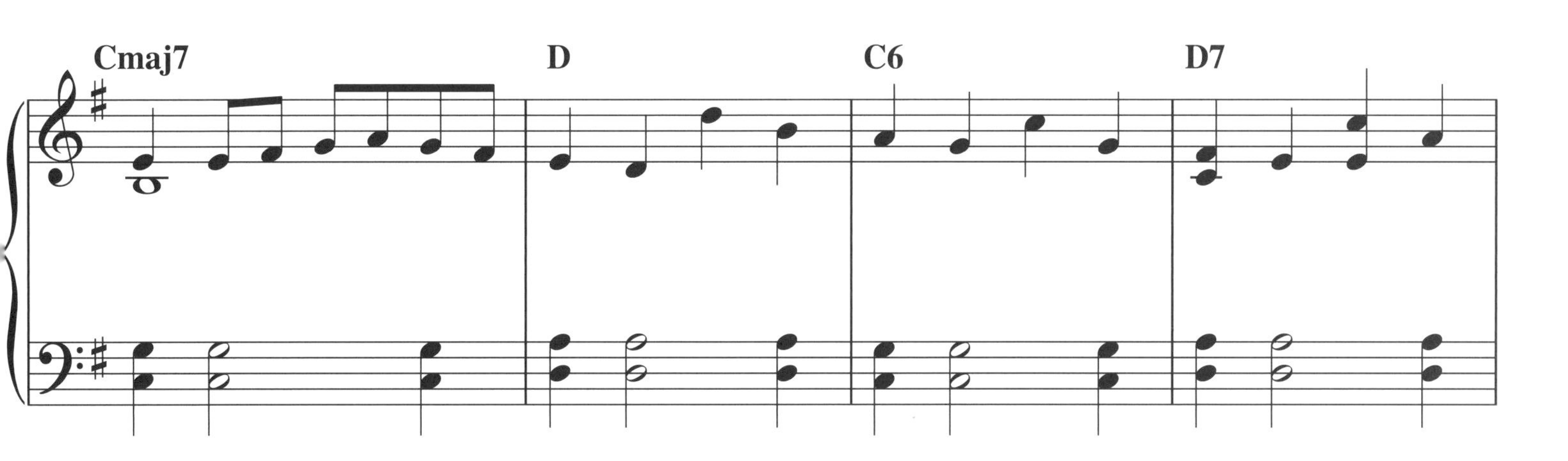
Cmaj7
D
C6
D7

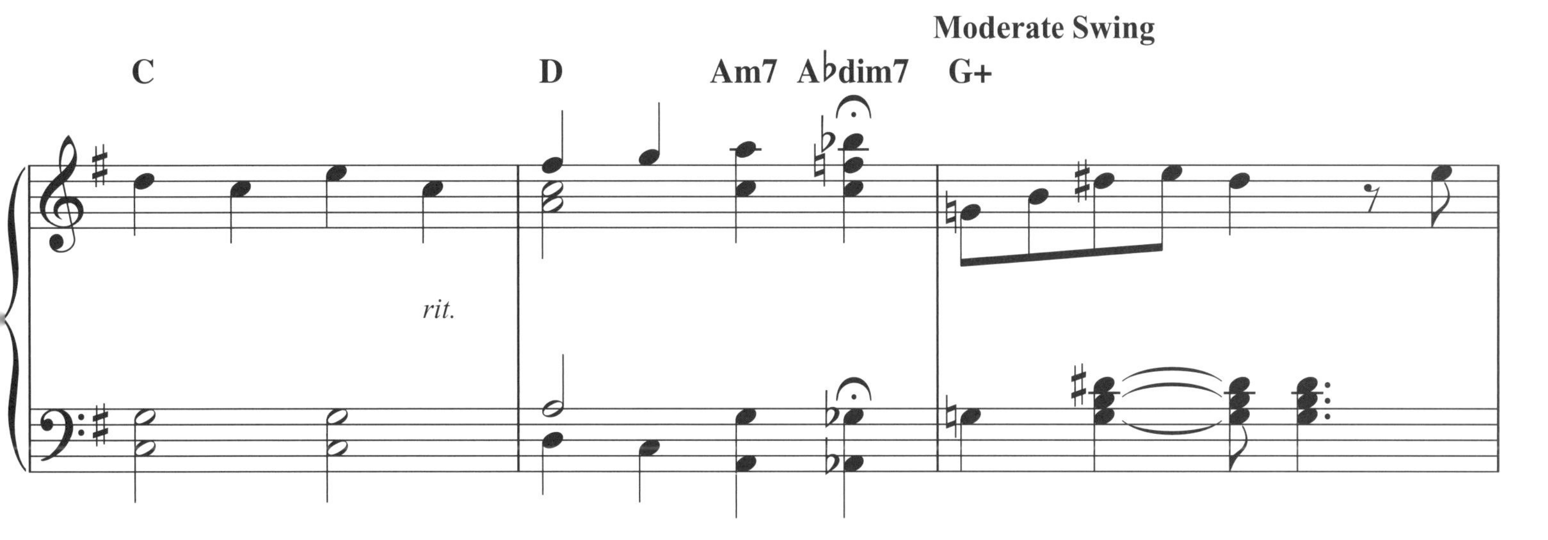
Moderate Swing
C
D
Am7
A♭dim7
G+
rit.

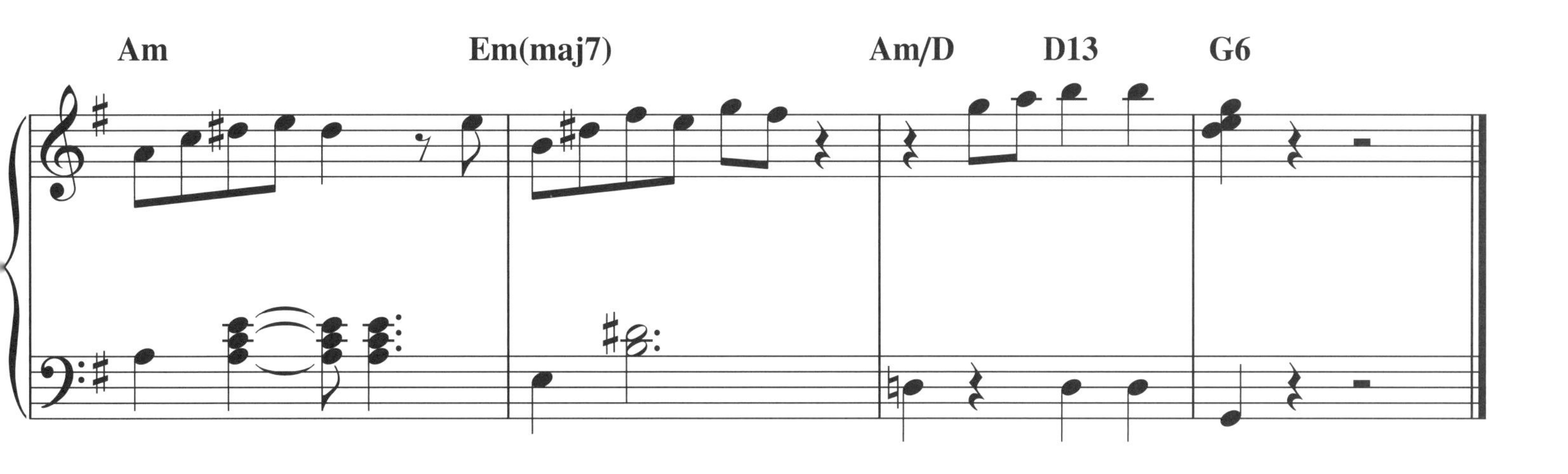
Am
Em(maj7)
Am/D
D13
G6

CITY OF STARS

Music by JUSTIN HURWITZ
Lyrics by BENJ PASEK & JUSTIN PAUL

Gm
C
C7
F
Am/E
knows?
I felt it from the first em - brace I shared with

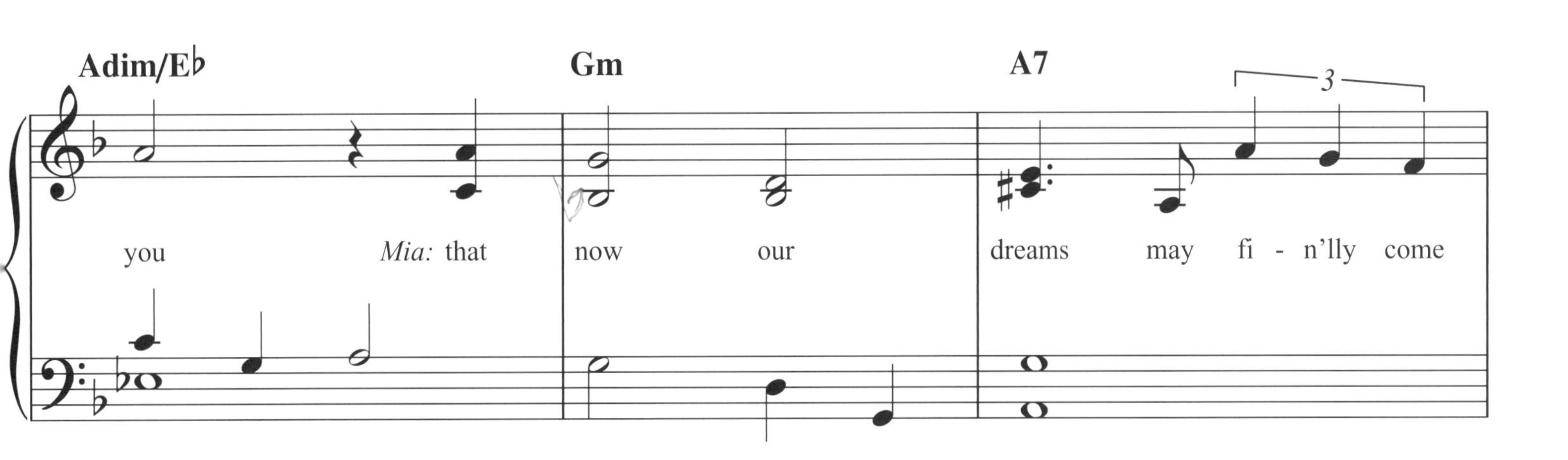
Adim/E♭
Gm
A7
3
you *Mia:* that now our dreams may fi - n'lly come

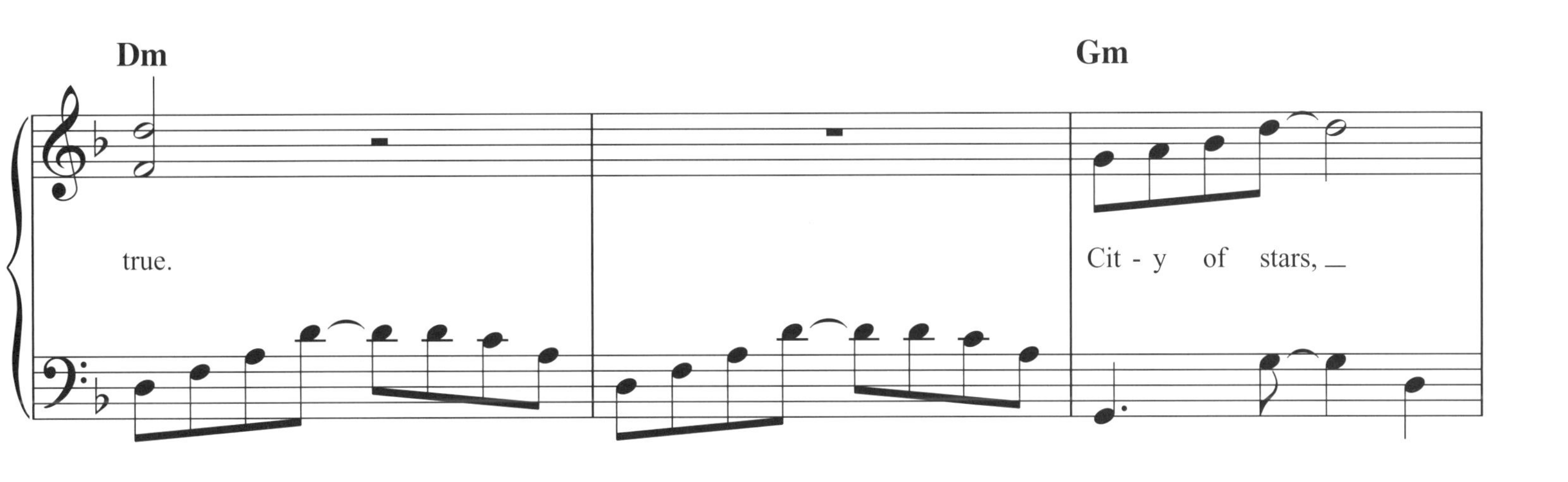
Dm
Gm
true.
Cit - y of stars,

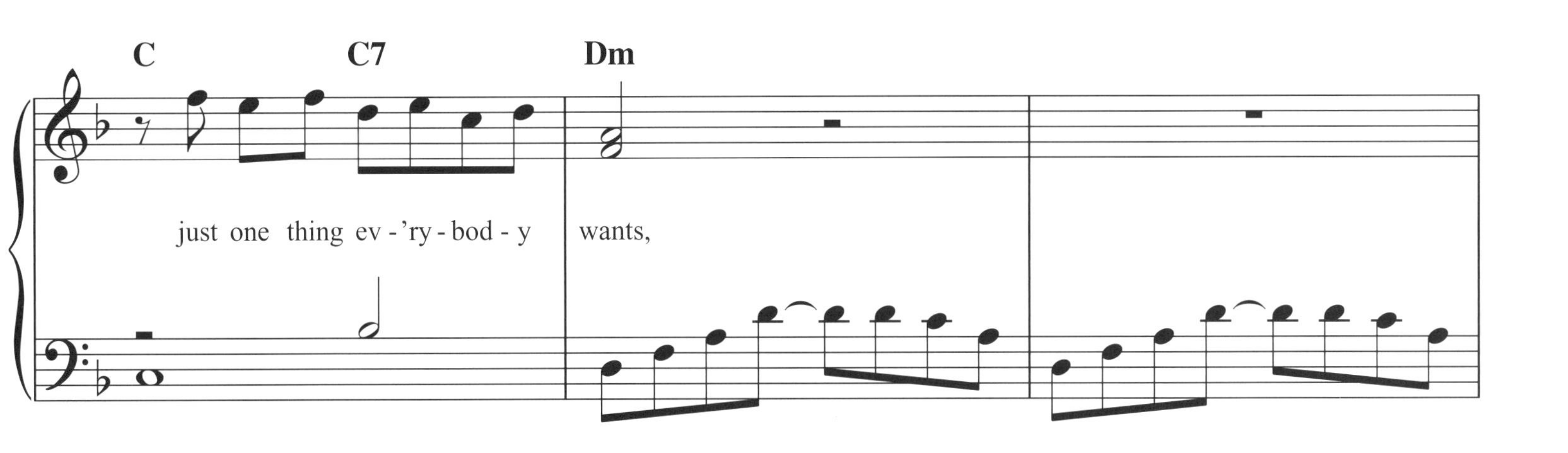
C
C7
Dm
just one thing ev - 'ry - bod - y wants,

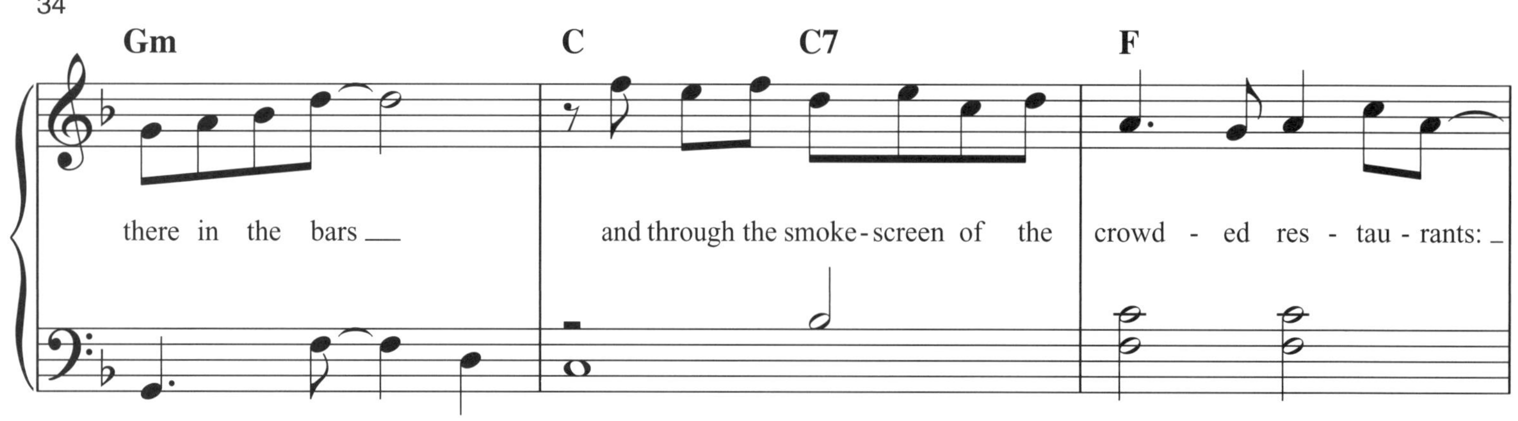
Gm
C
C7
F
there in the bars
and through the smoke-screen of the
crowd - ed res - tau - rants:

F/E
Gm
C
C7
it's
love.
Yes, all we're look-ing for is

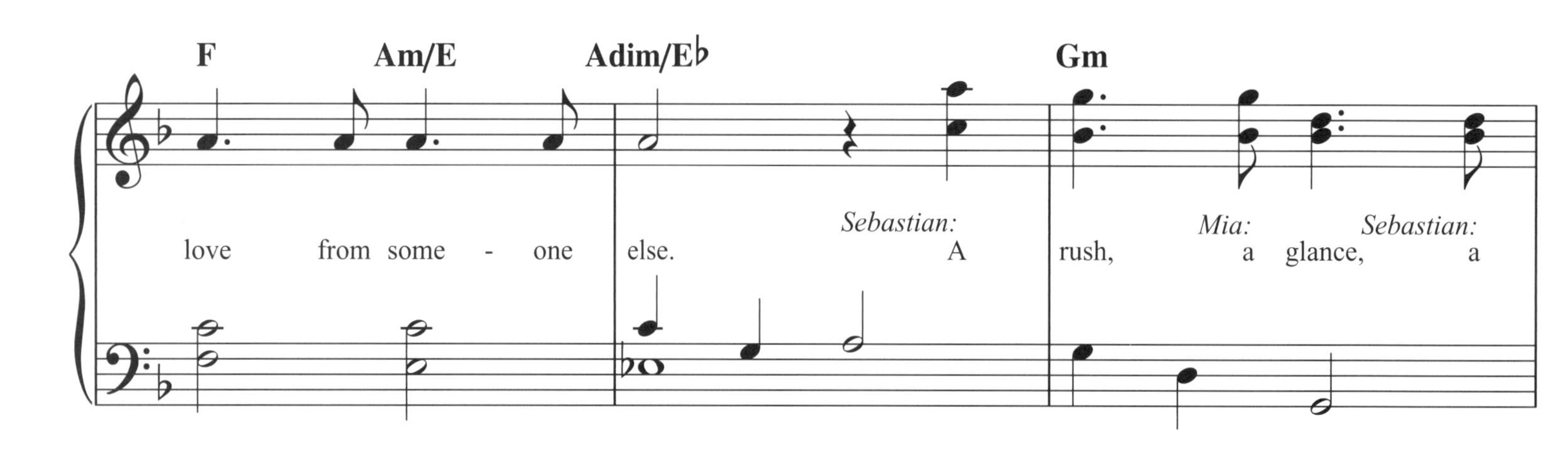
F
Am/E
Adim/E♭
Gm
love from some - one
else.
Sebastian:
A
rush,
Mia:
a glance,
Sebastian:
a

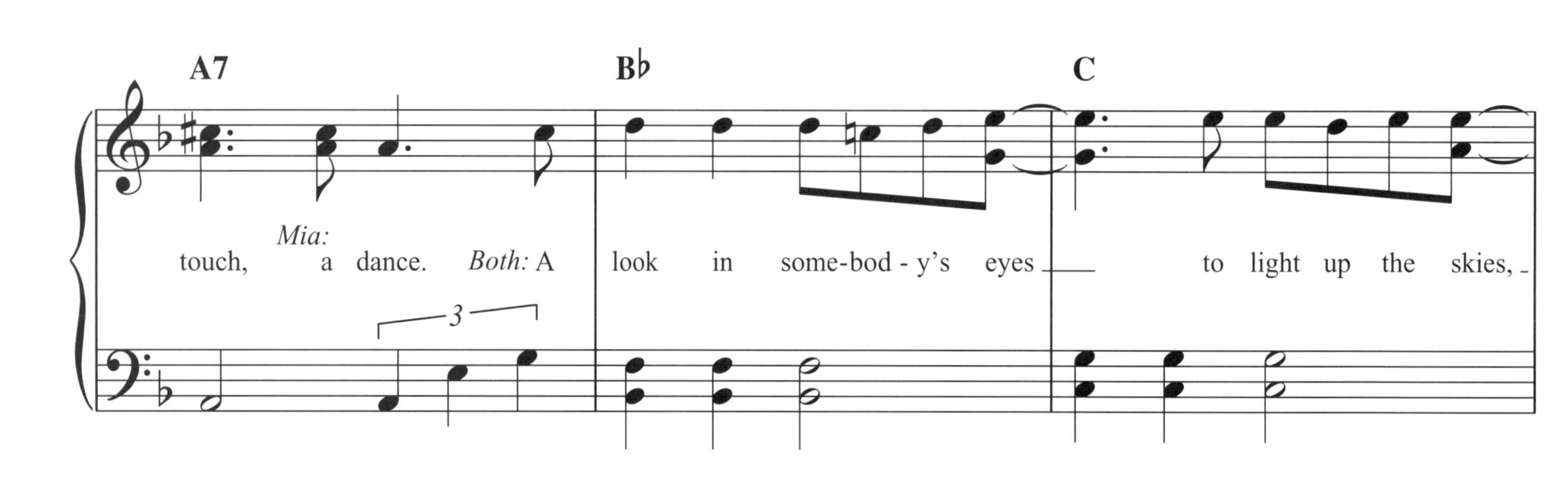
A7
B♭
C
touch,
Mia:
a dance.
Both: A
look in some-bod - y's eyes
to light up the skies,
3

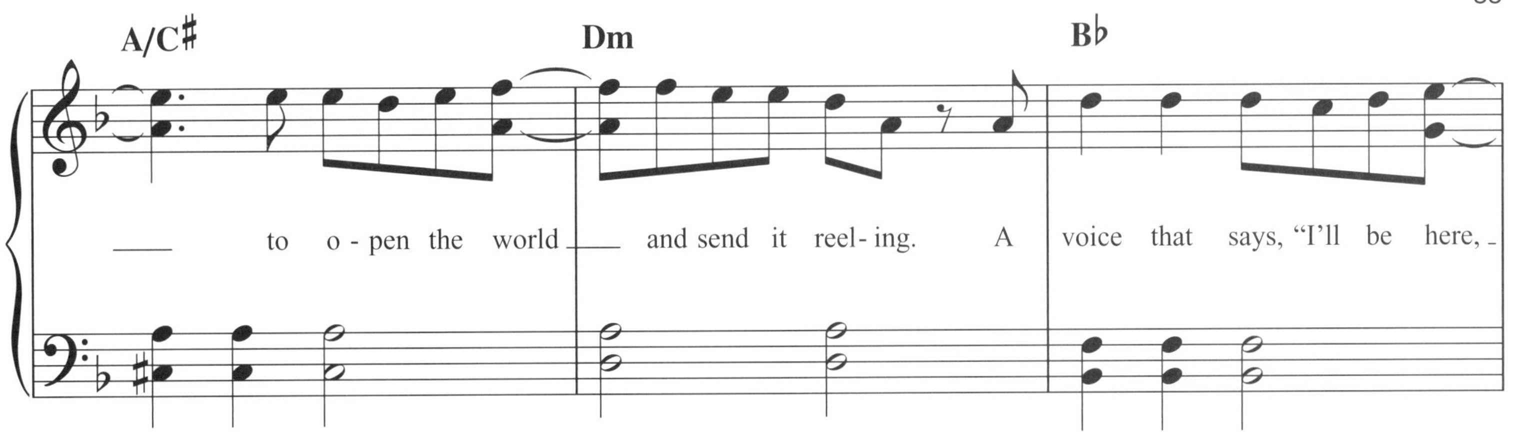
A/C♯
Dm
B♭
to o - pen the world and send it reel - ing. A voice that says, "I'll be here,

C
Dm
and you'll be al - right."

B♭
C
A/C♯
I don't care if I know just where I will go, 'cause all that I need's

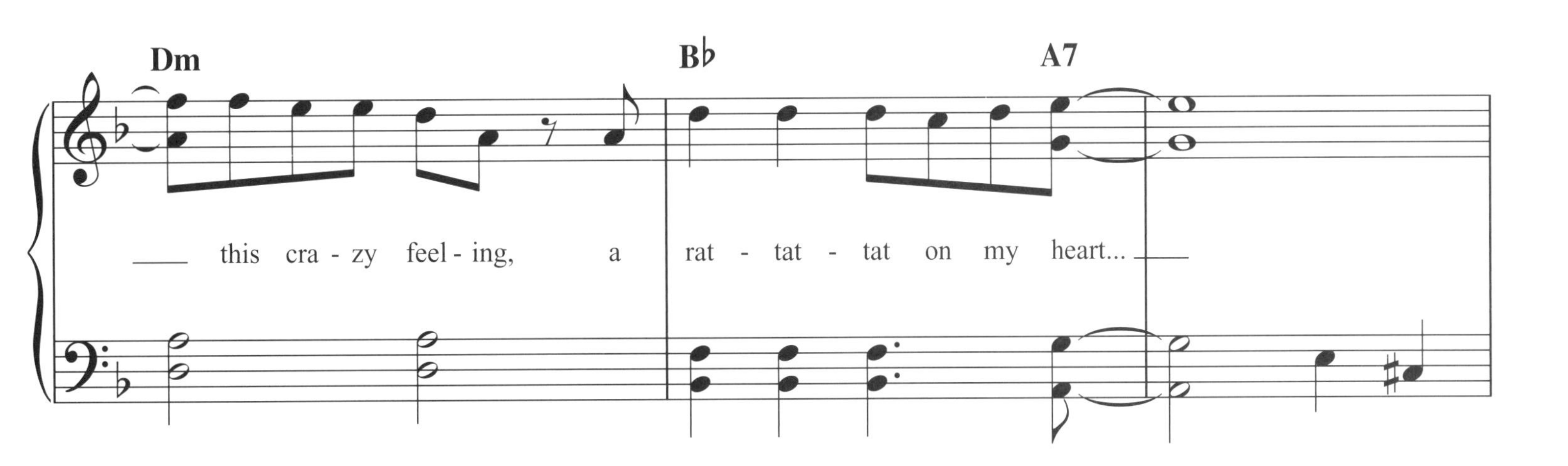
Dm
B♭
A7
this cra - zy feel - ing, a rat - tat - tat on my heart...

Freely
Dm
Sebastian: Think I want it to
stay.

Gm
C7
F
Cit - y of stars,
are you shin - ing just for
me?

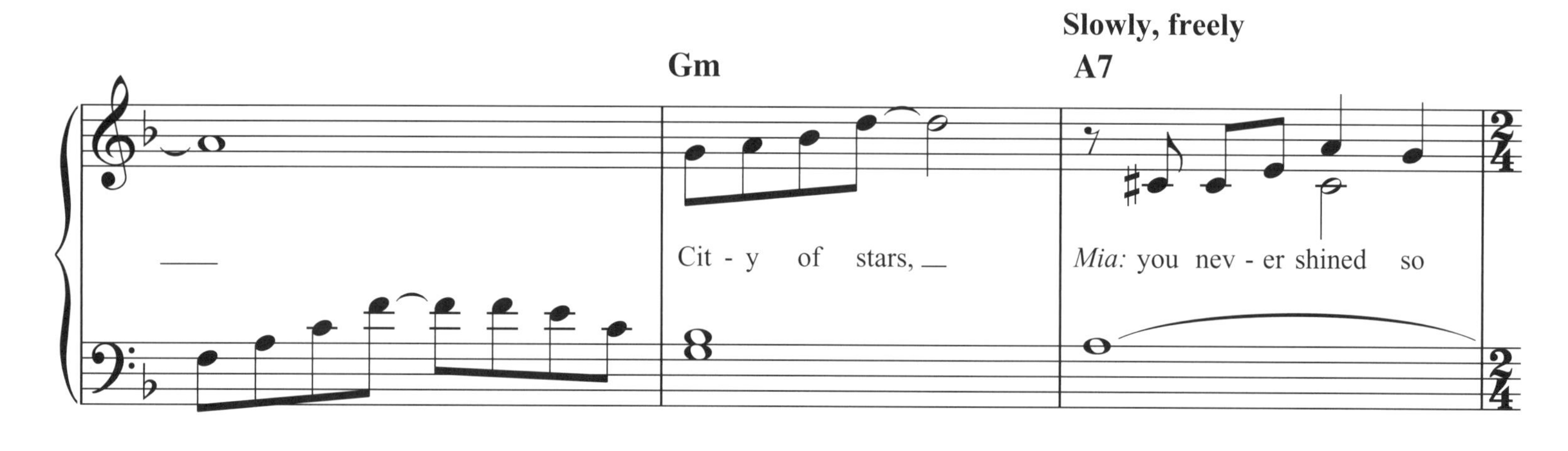
Gm
Slowly, freely
A7
Cit - y of stars,
Mia: you nev - er shined so

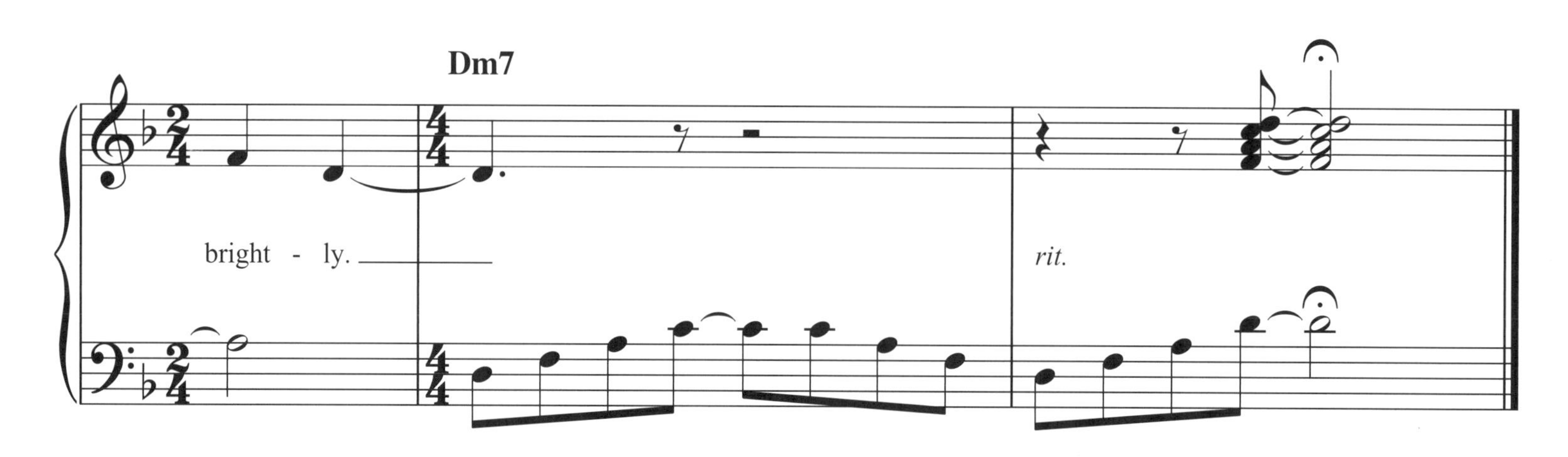
Dm7
bright - ly.
rit.

PLANETARIUM

Music by
JUSTIN HURWITZ

E6
A♭7
8va
(8va)
E6
A♭7
8va
Adim7
8va

Gdim
8va
8va
D7/F♯
8va
D7
8va

Slightly faster
G6
Am7
D7/F♯
Gmaj7

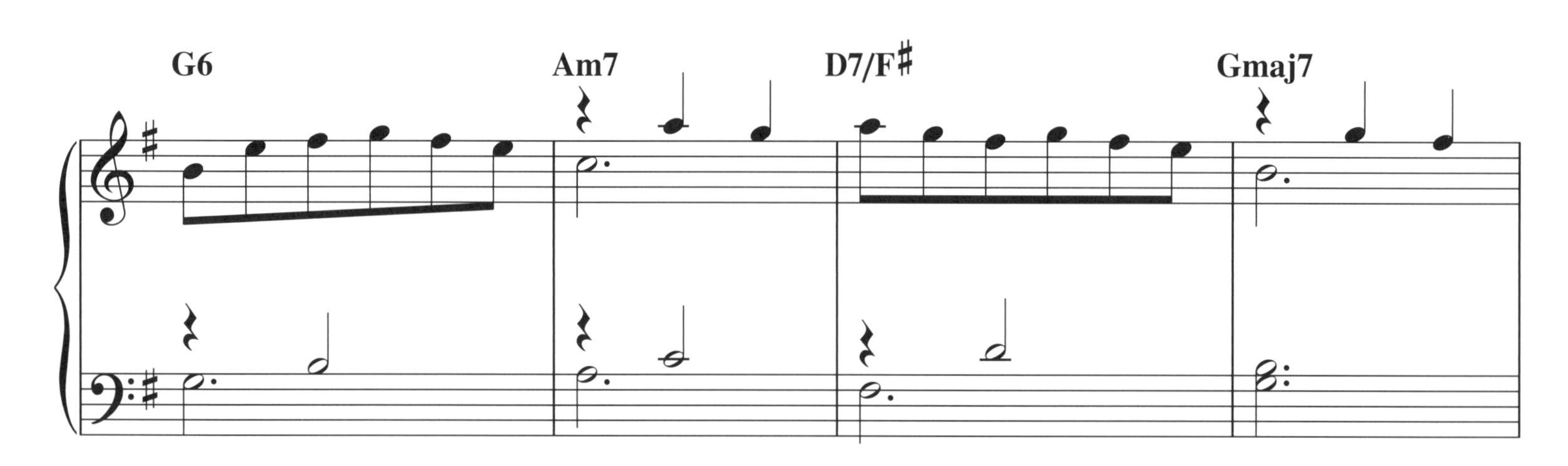
G6
Am7
D7/F♯
Gmaj7

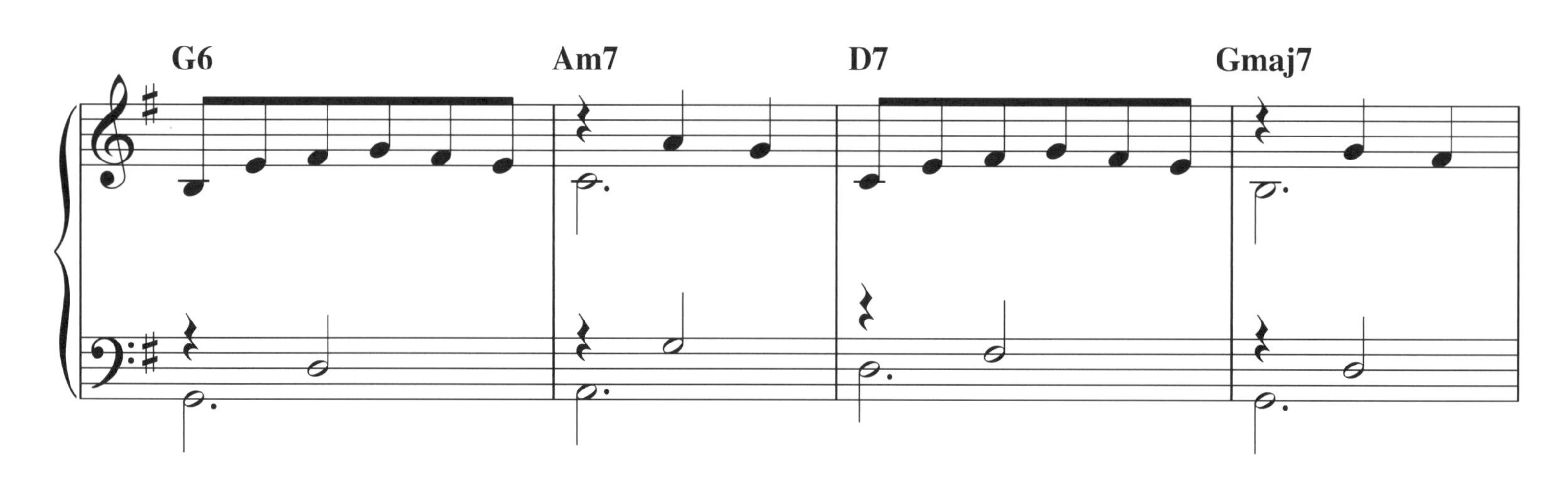
G6
Am7
D7
Gmaj7

G6
Am7
D7
Gmaj7

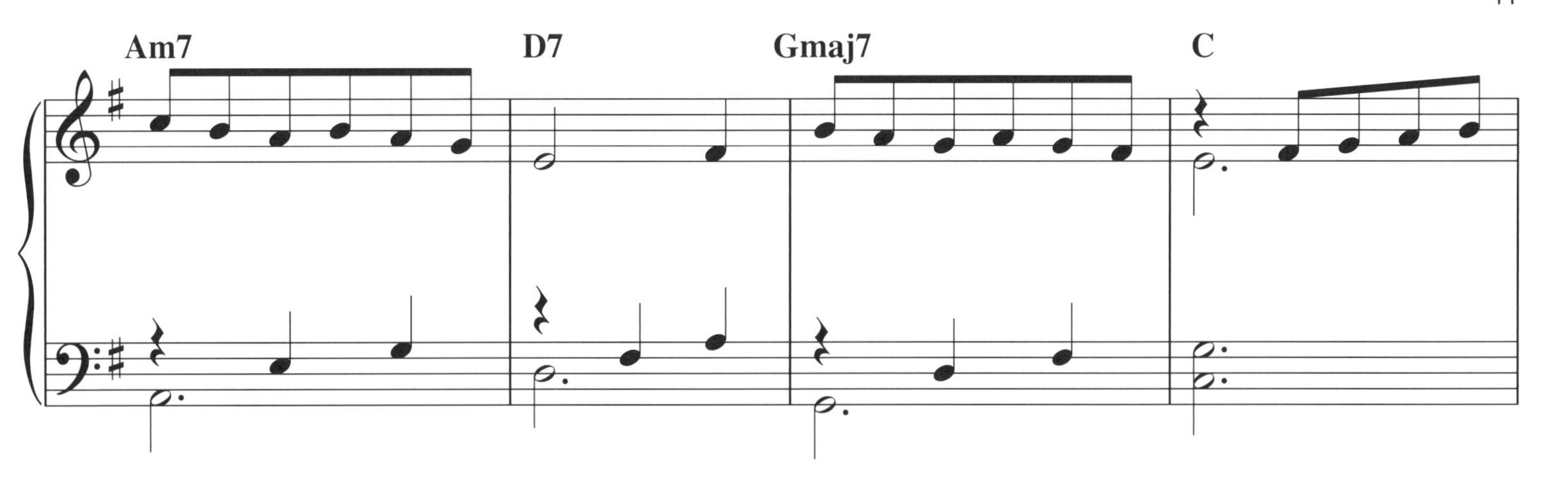
Am7
D7
Gmaj7
C

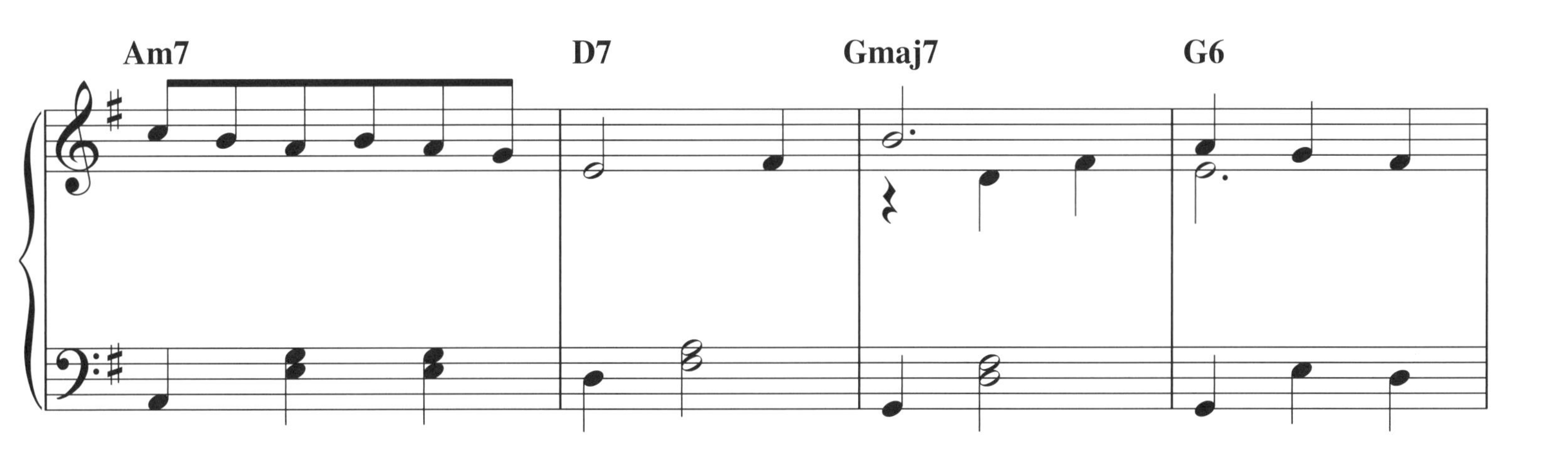
Am7
D7
Gmaj7
G6

Am7
D
B7/D♯
Em

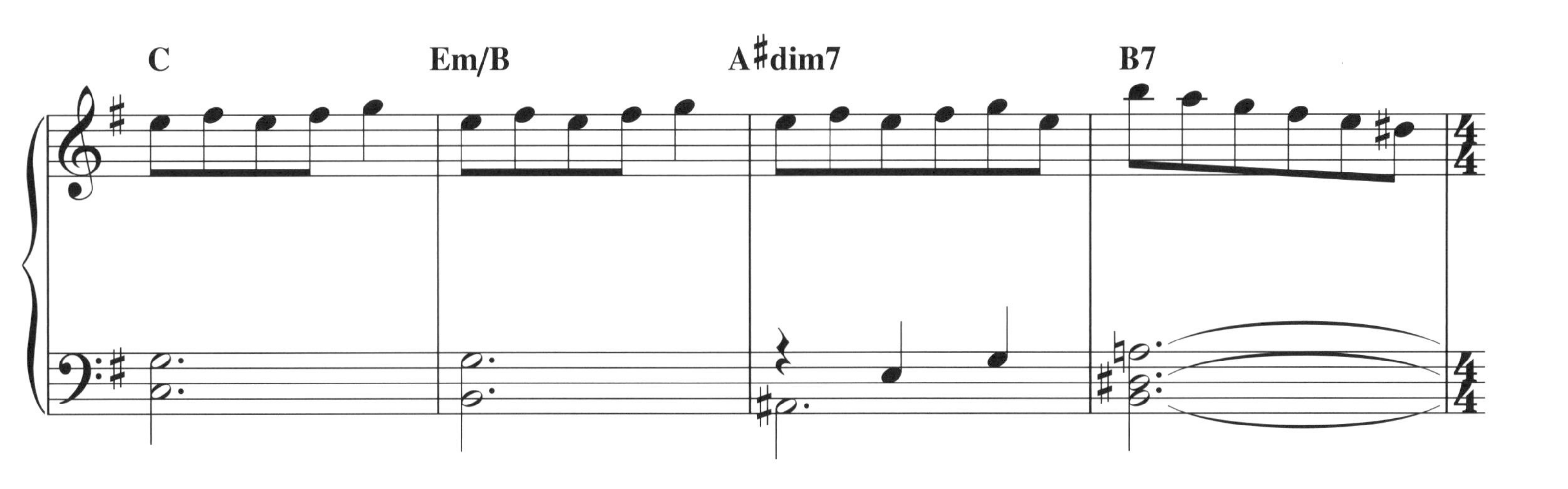
C
Em/B
A♯dim7
B7

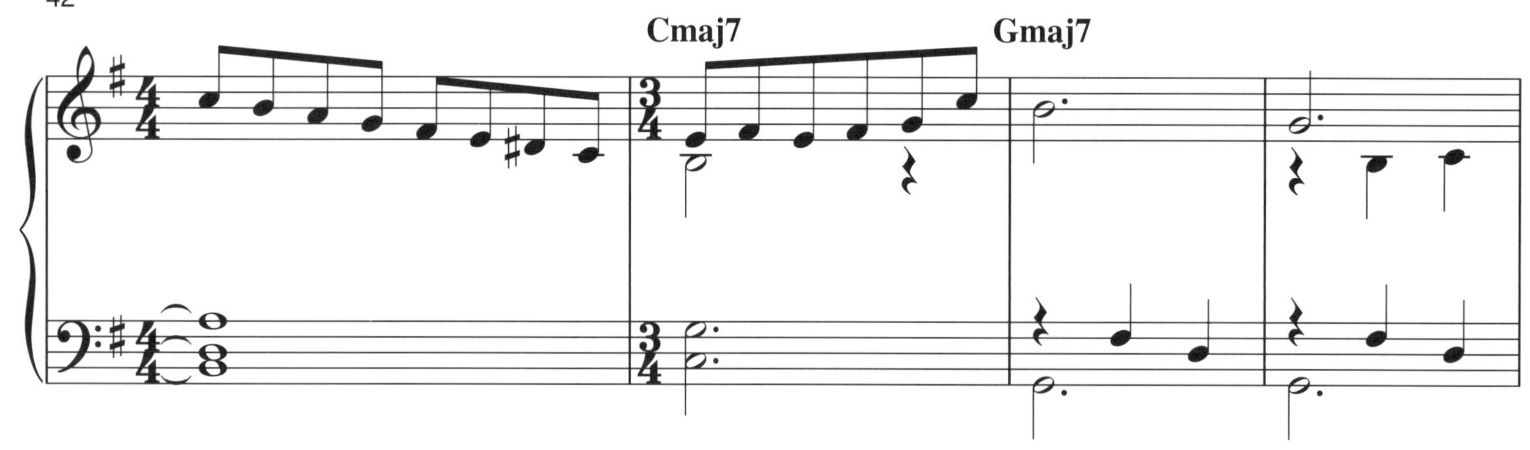
Cmaj7
Gmaj7

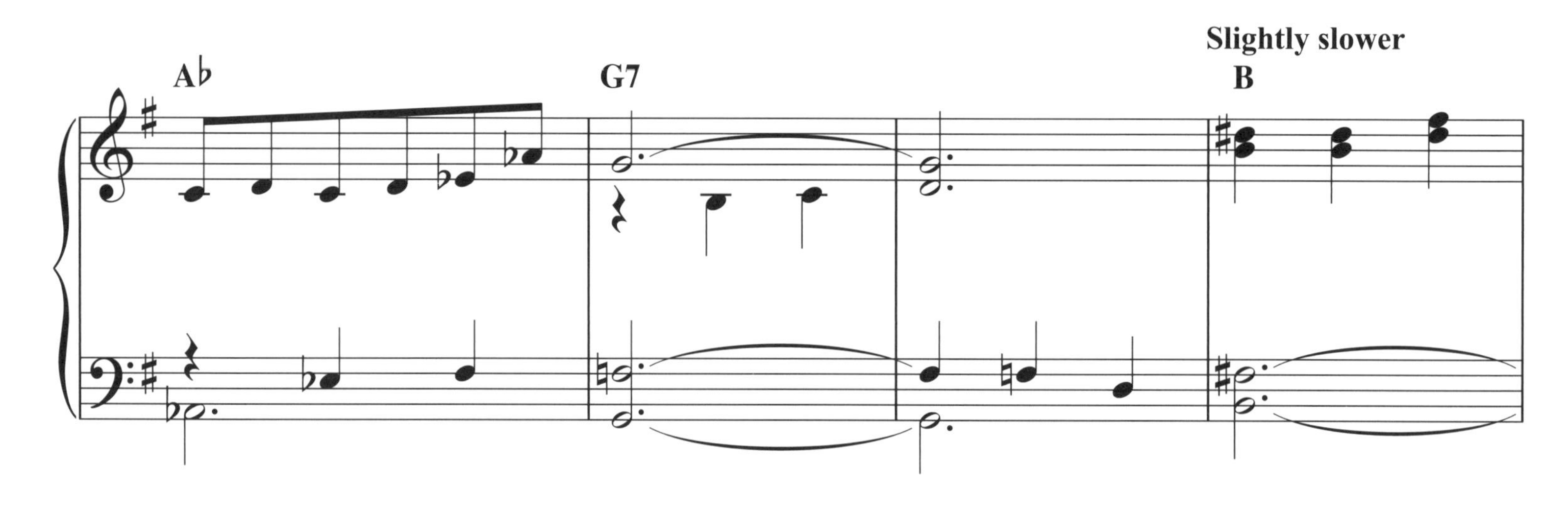
Slightly slower
A♭
G7
B

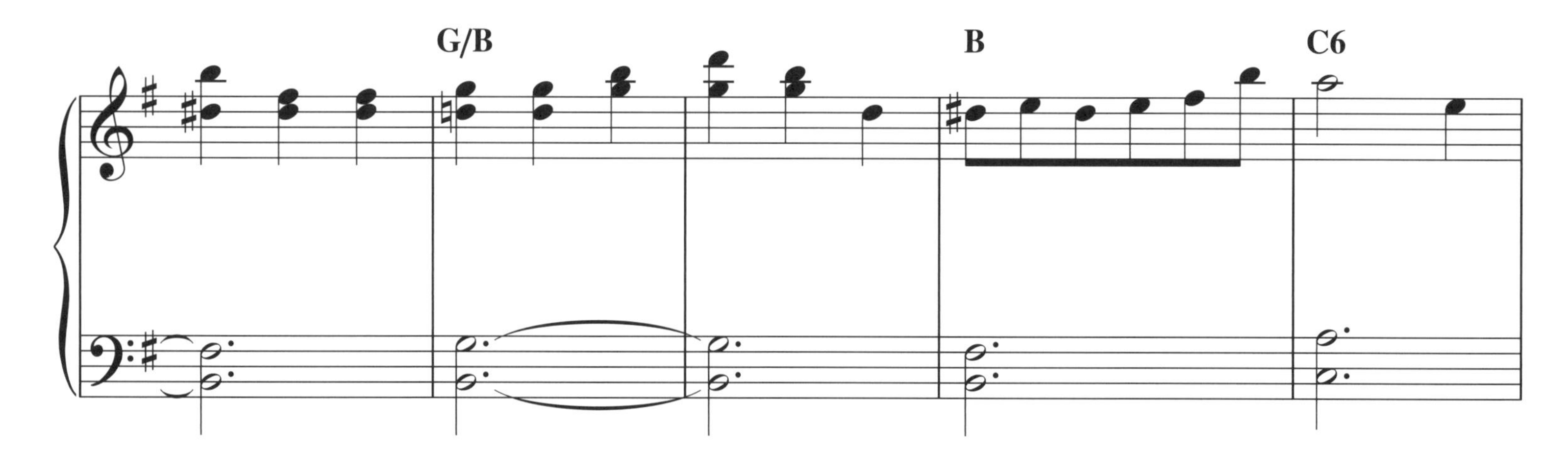
G/B
B
C6

B
C

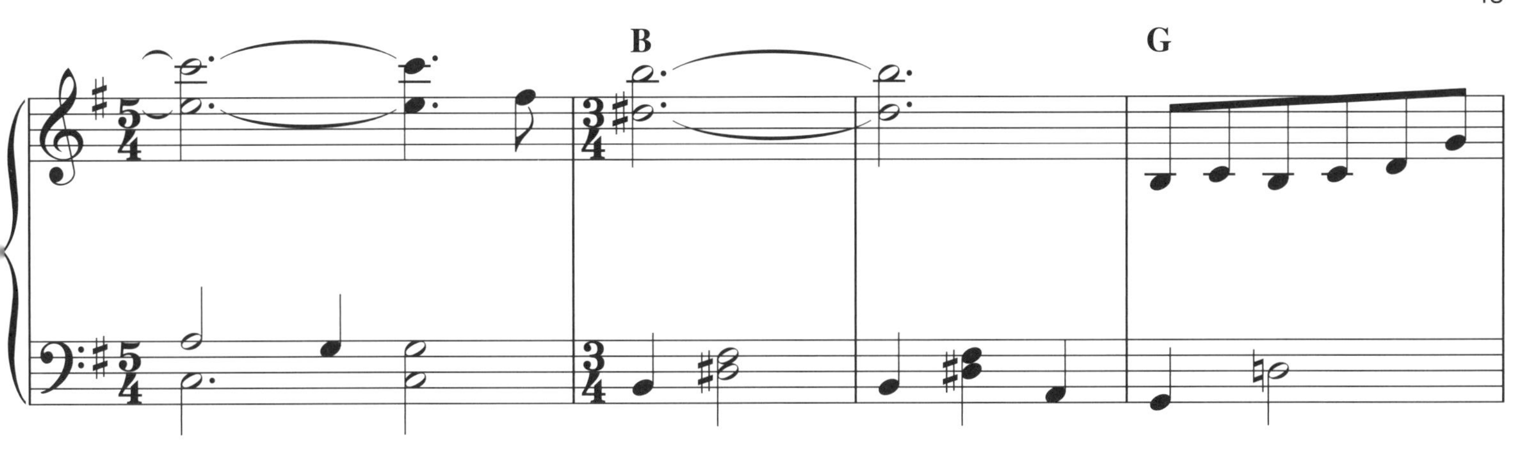
B
G

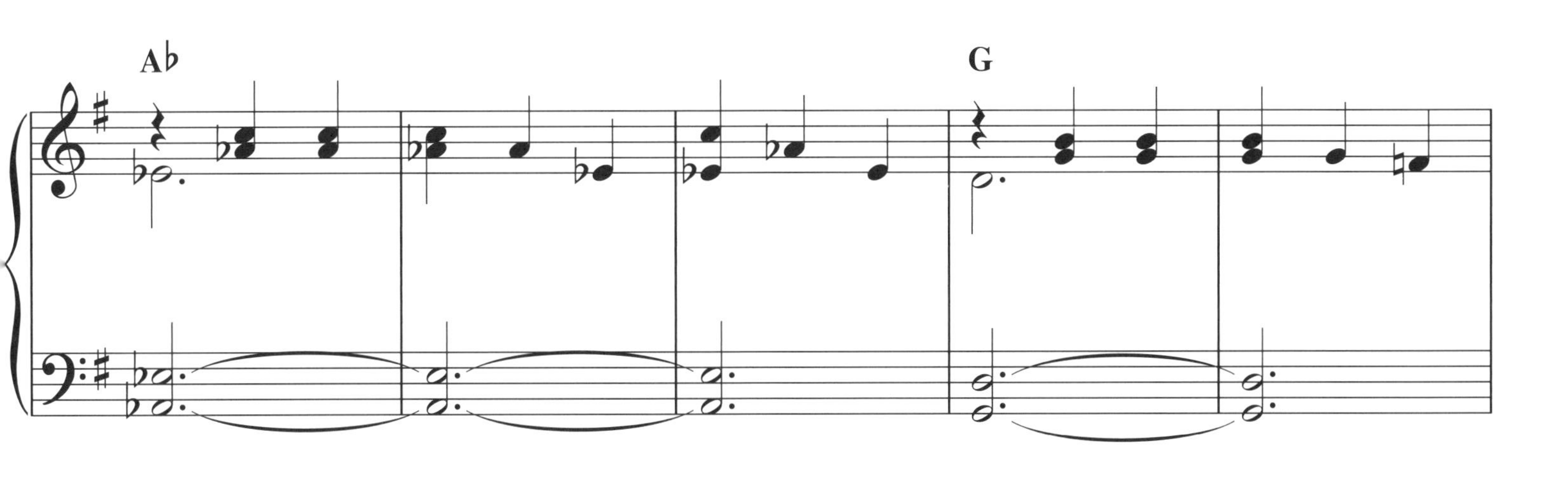
A♭
G

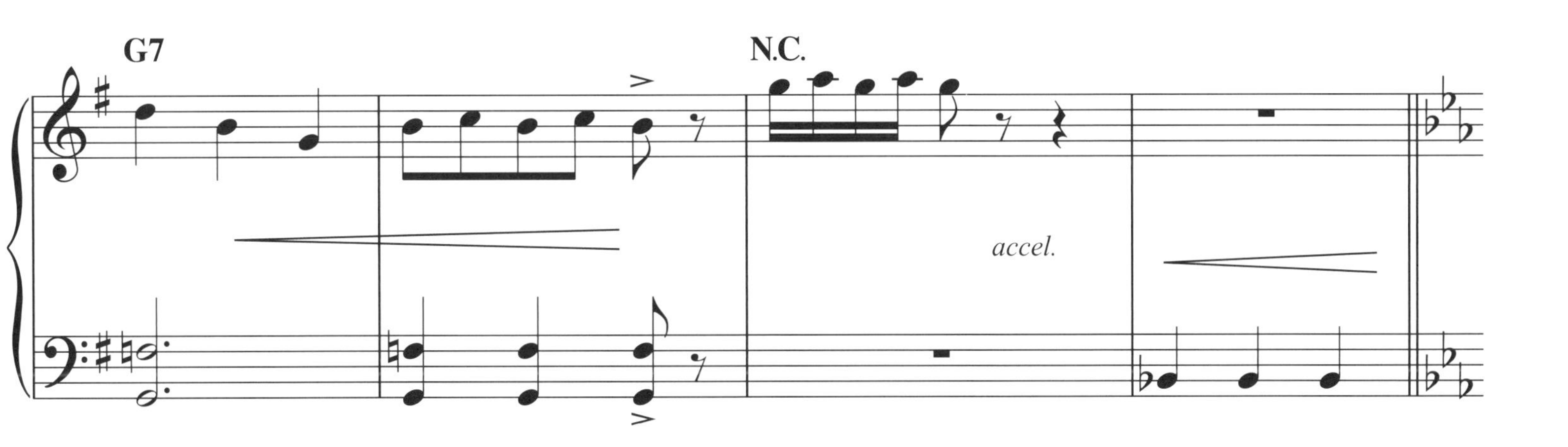
G7
N.C.
accel.

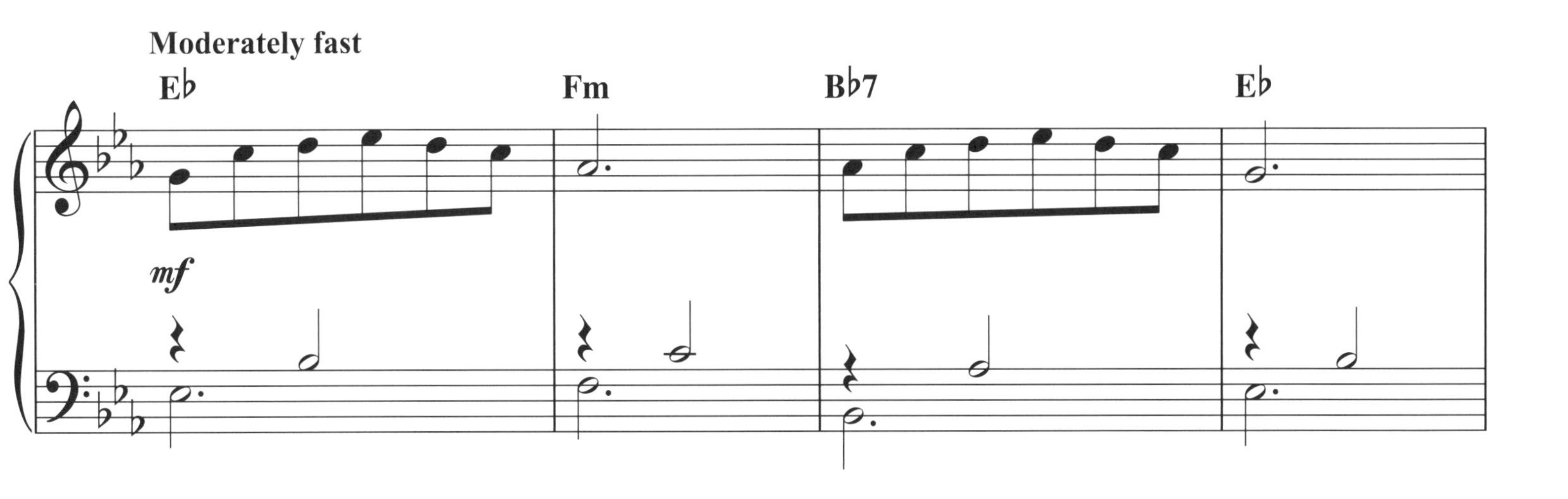
Moderately fast
E♭
Fm
B♭7
E♭
mf

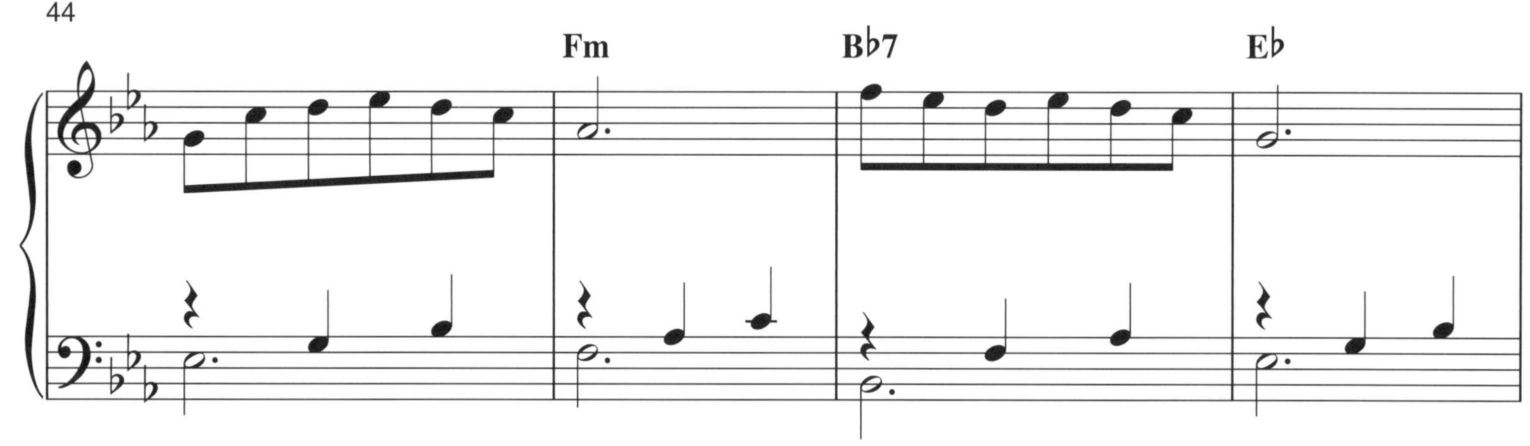

Fm
B♭7
E♭

Fm
B♭7
E♭

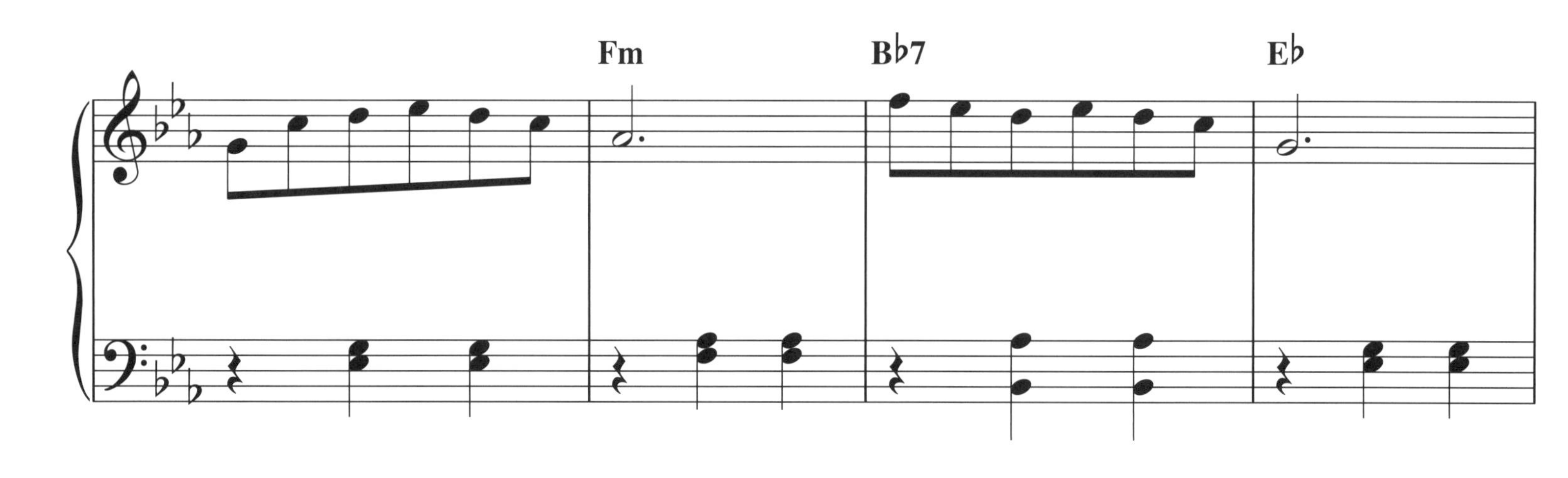

Fm
B♭7
E♭

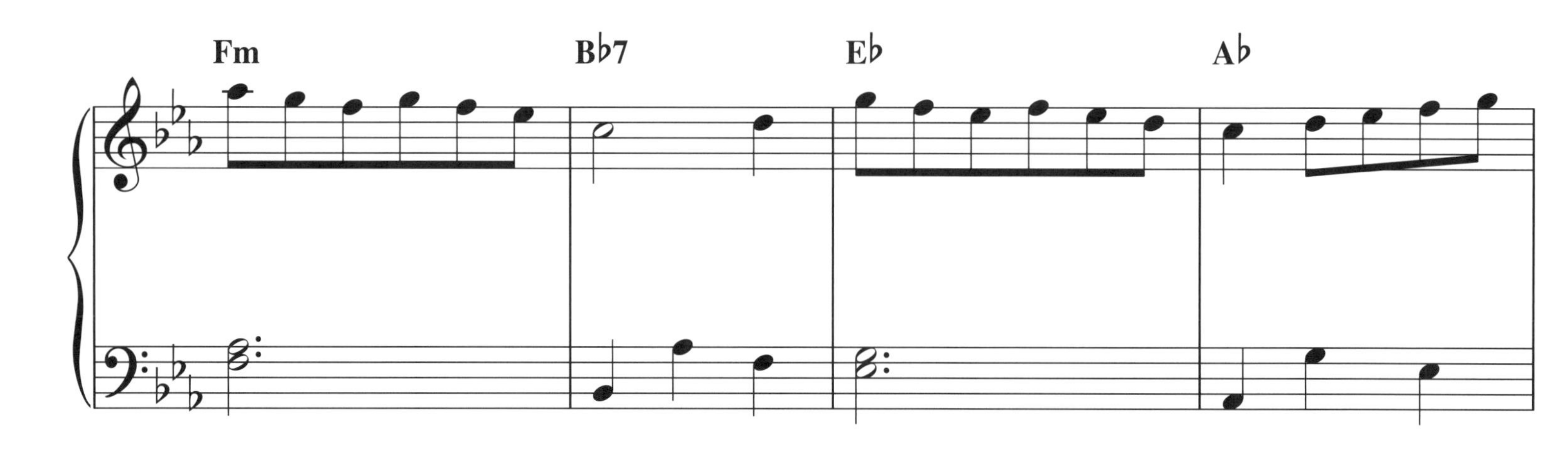

Fm
B♭7
E♭
A♭

Fm
B♭7
E♭
E♭/D

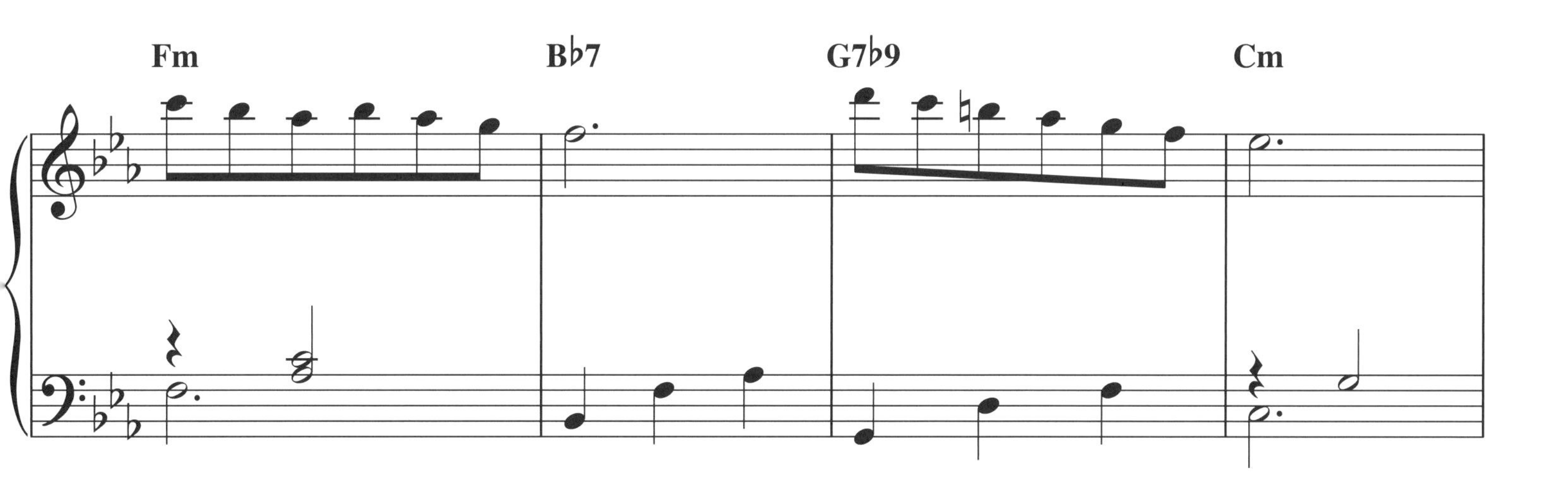
Fm
B♭7
G7♭9
Cm

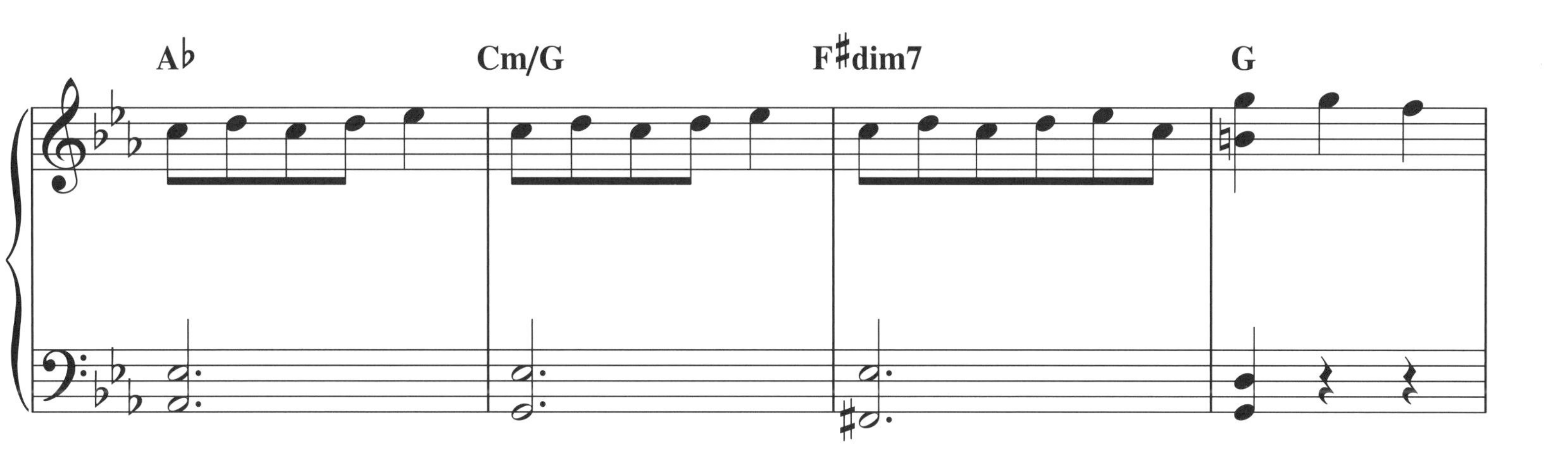
A♭
Cm/G
F♯dim7
G

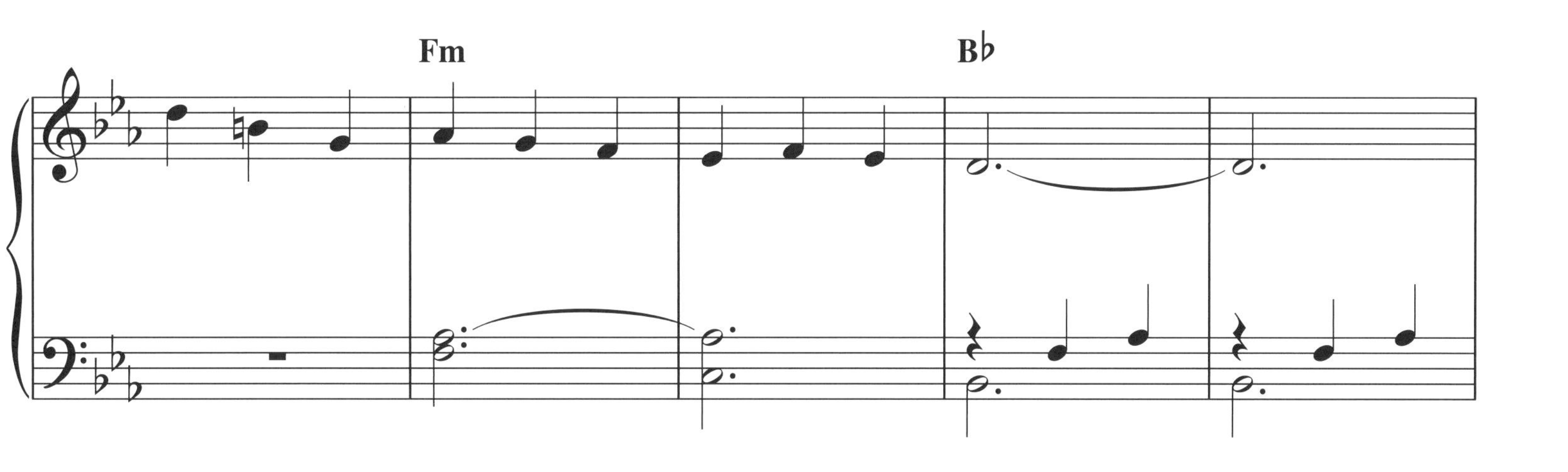
Fm
B♭

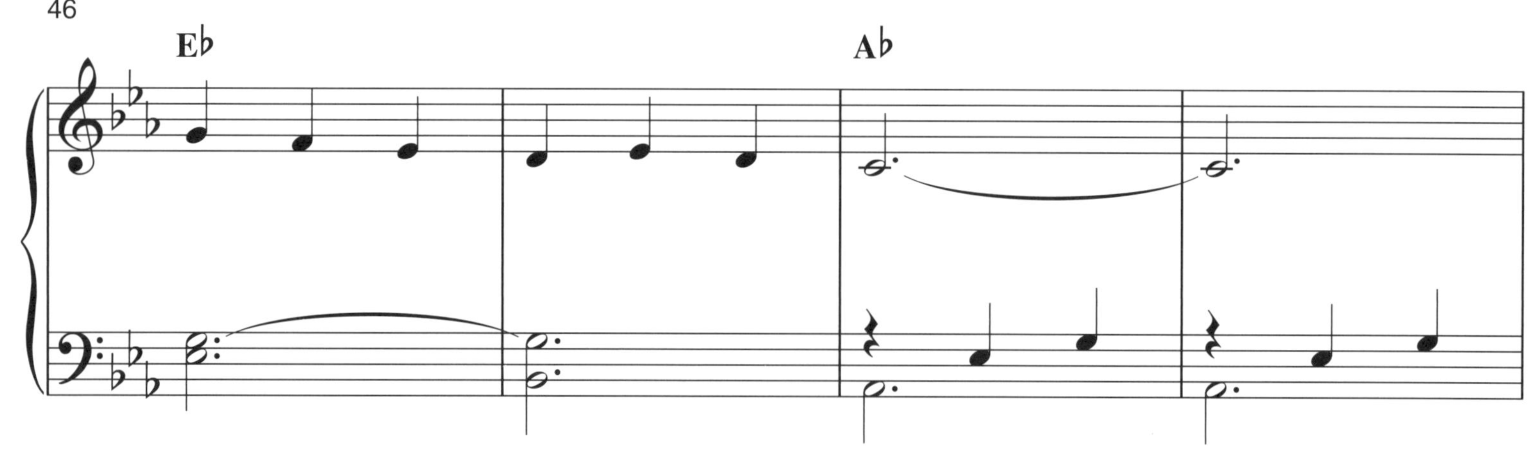
E♭
A♭

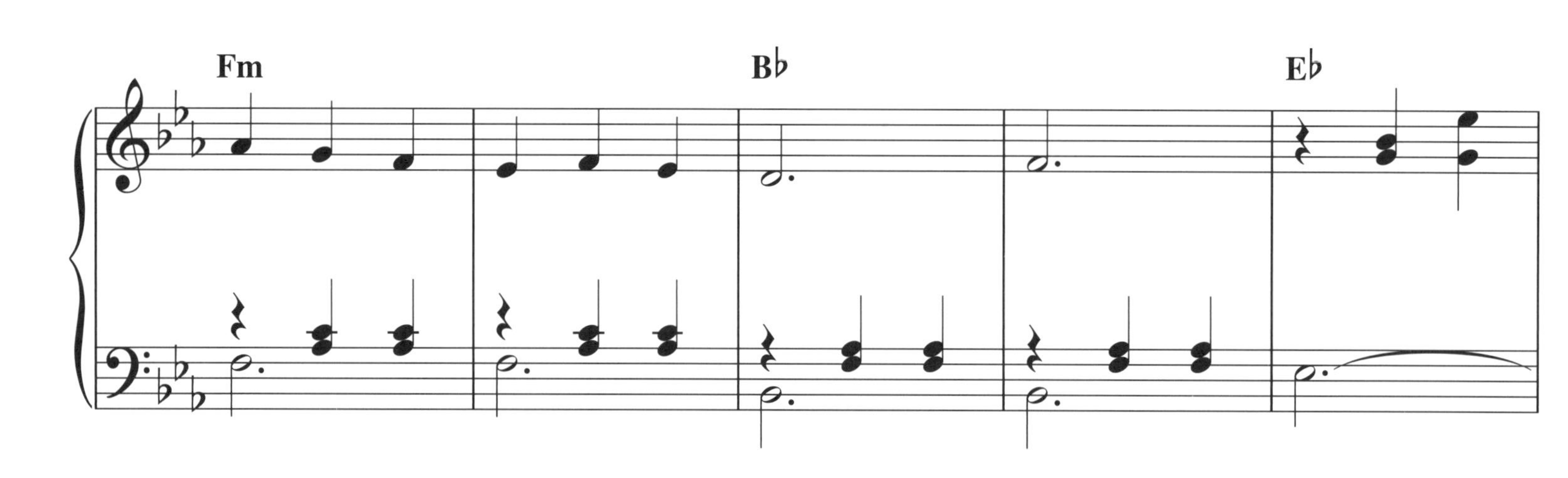
Fm
B♭
E♭

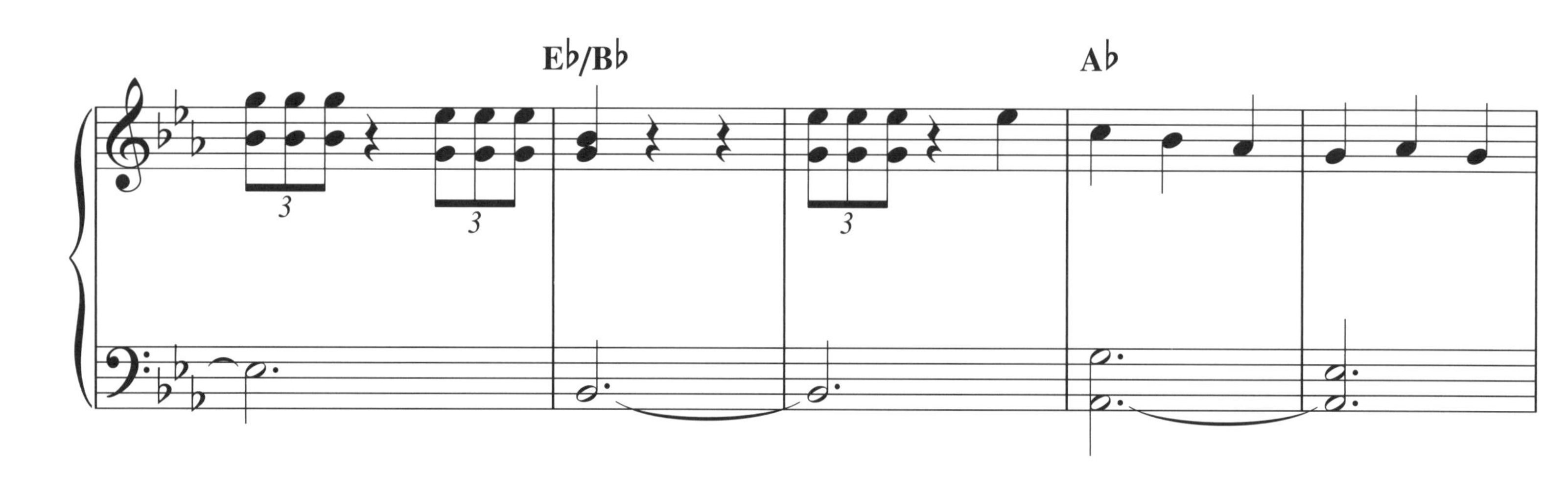
E♭/B♭
A♭
3
3
3

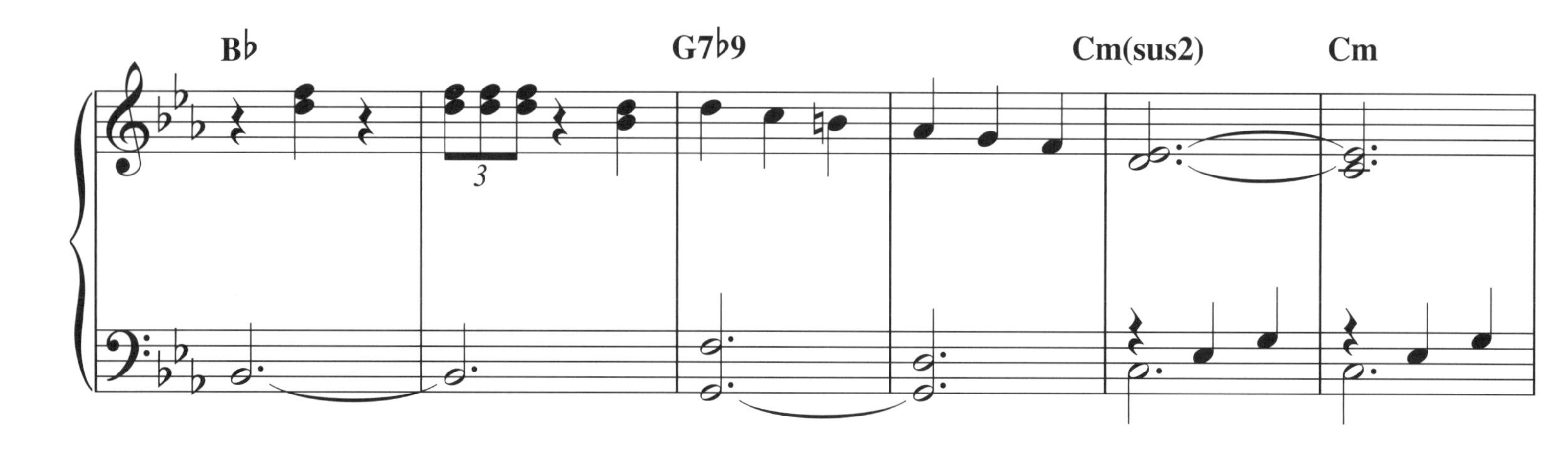
B♭
G7♭9
Cm(sus2)
Cm
3

A♭
mp
A♭6

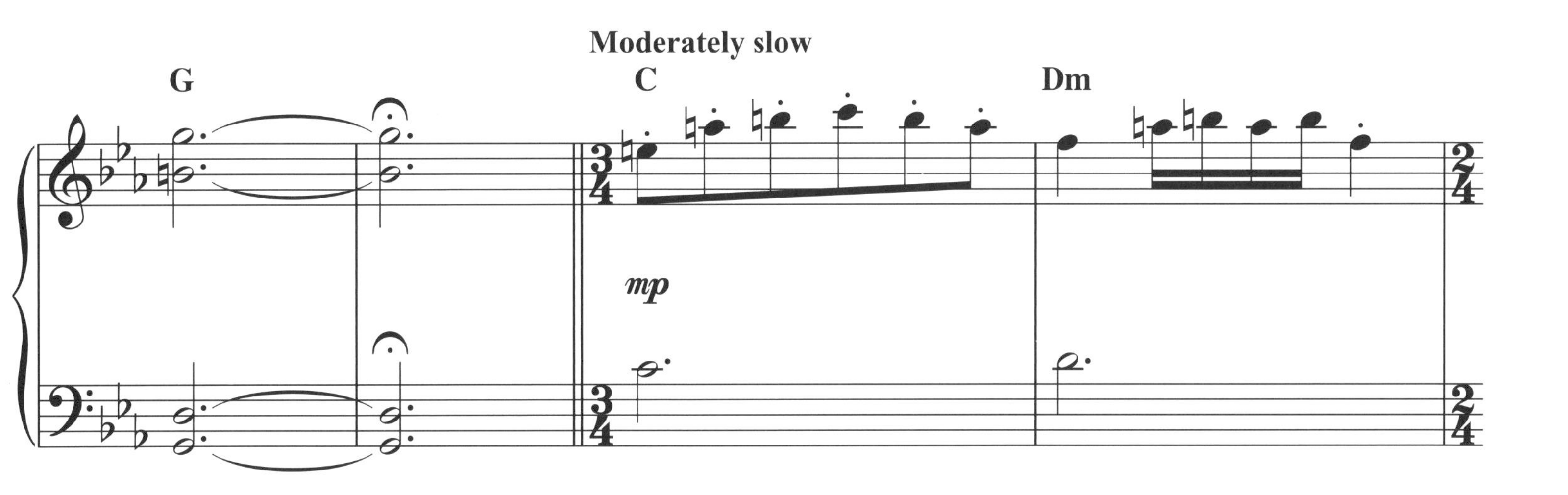
Moderately slow
G
C
Dm
mp

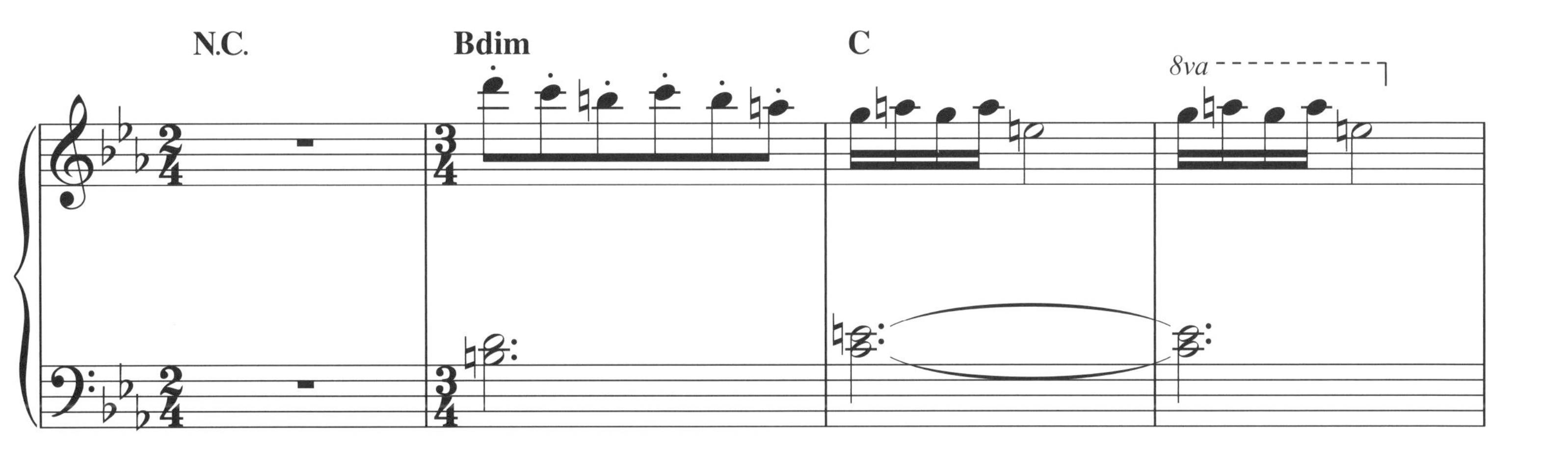
N.C.
Bdim
C
8va

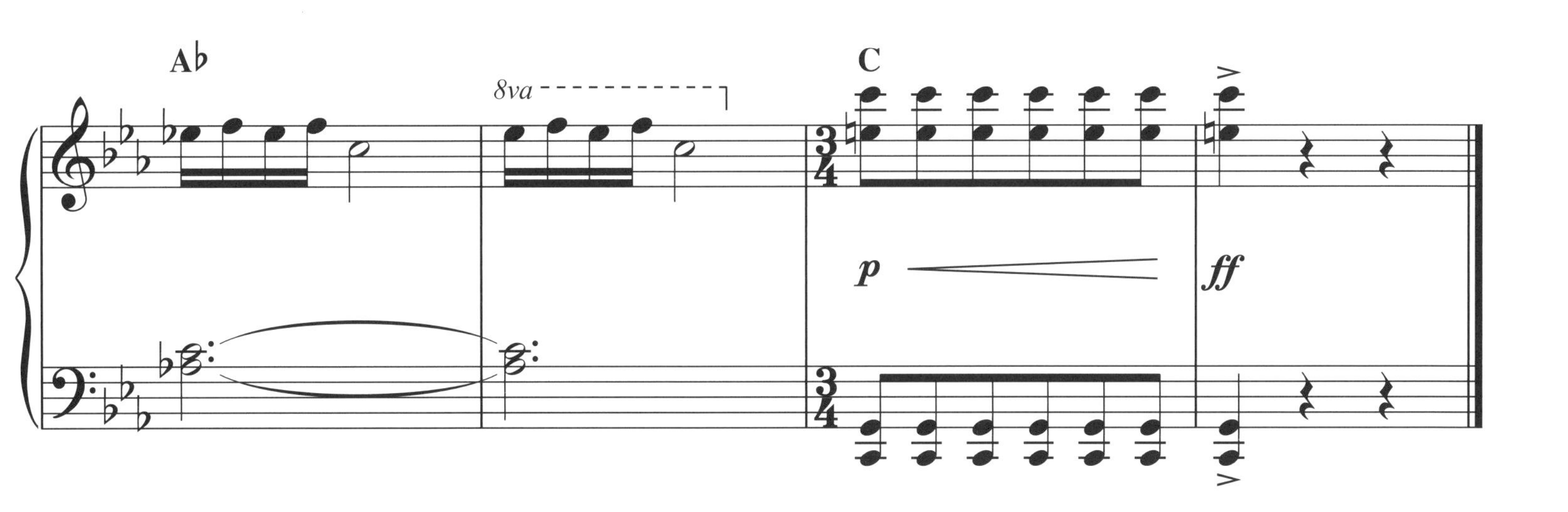
A♭
8va
C
p
ff

START A FIRE

Music & Lyrics by JOHN STEPHENS,
ANGÉLIQUE CINÉLU, MARIUS de VRIES
and JUSTIN HURWITZ

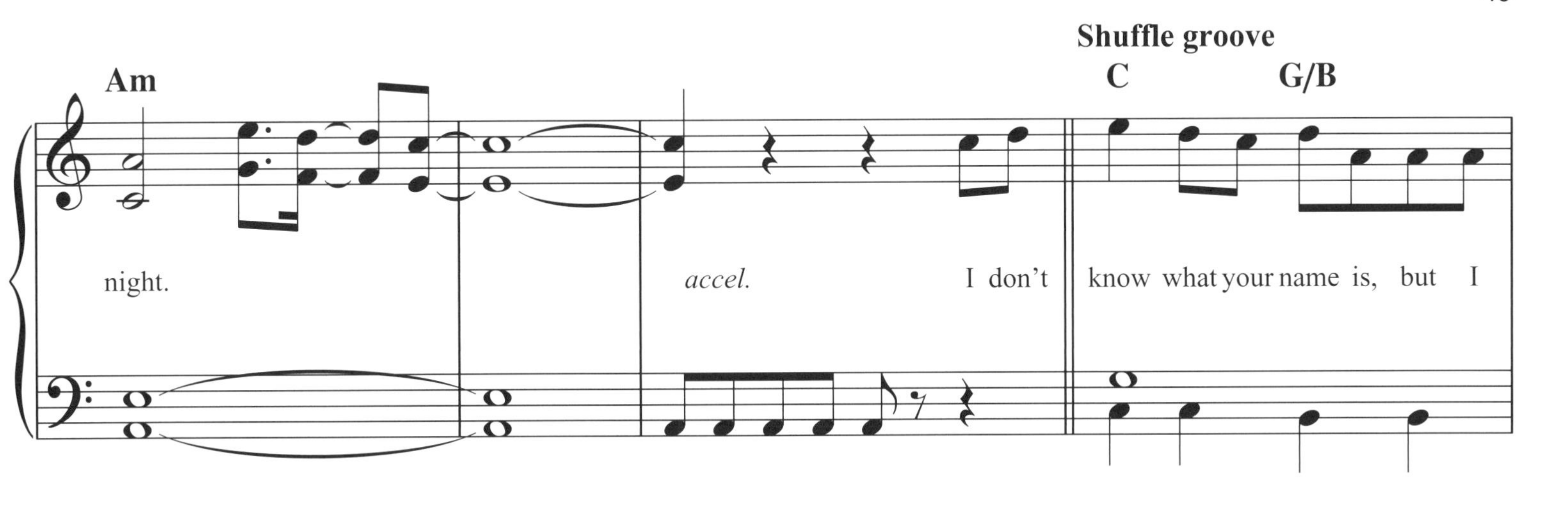
Shuffle groove
Am
C
G/B
night.
accel.
I don't
know what your name is, but I

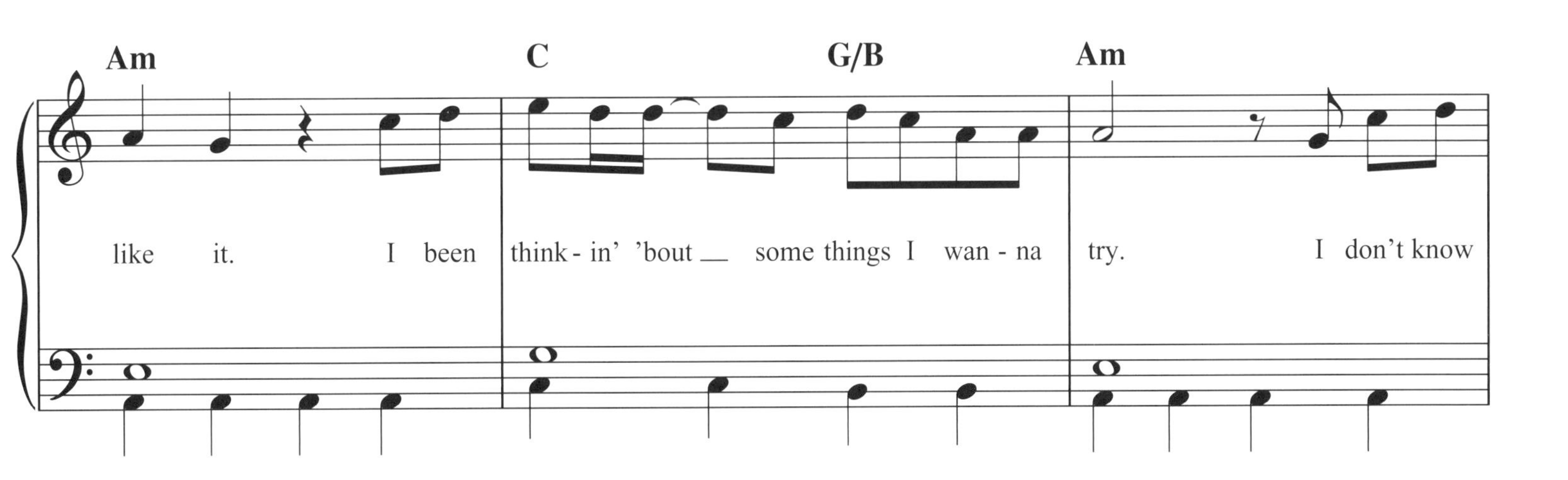
Am
C
G/B
Am
like it. I been
think - in' 'bout some things I wan - na
try. I don't know

C
G/B
Am
F/C
G/B
what you came to do, but I
want to do it with you. And
I just know I feel so good to -

Am
F
Am
F
night. Oh,
if we keep on
danc - ing, take the
rhy - thm to new

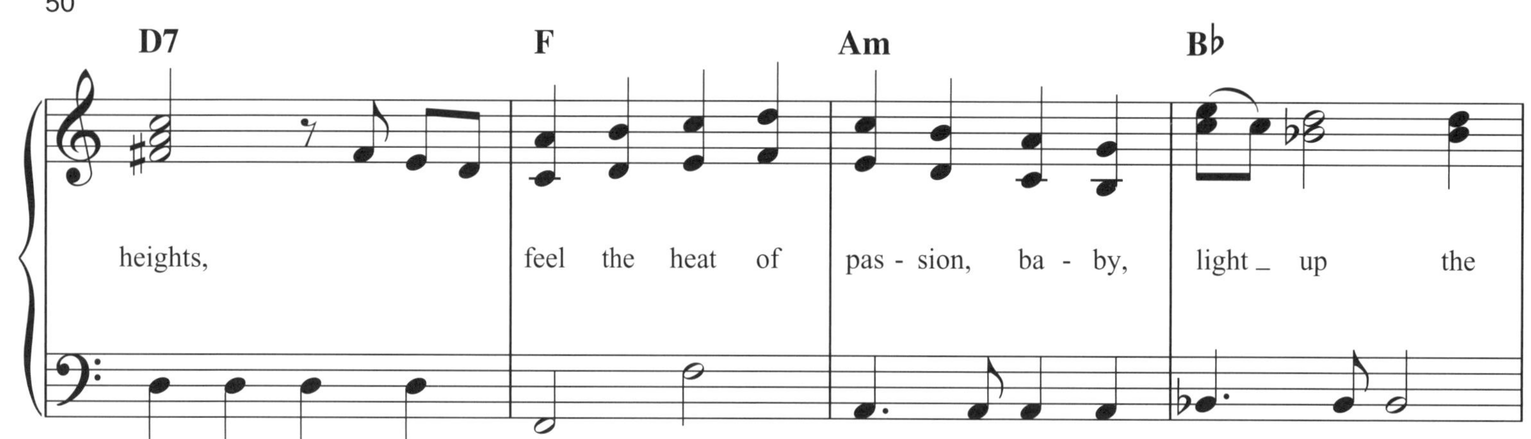
D7
F
Am
B♭
heights,
feel the heat of
pas - sion, ba - by,
light _ up the

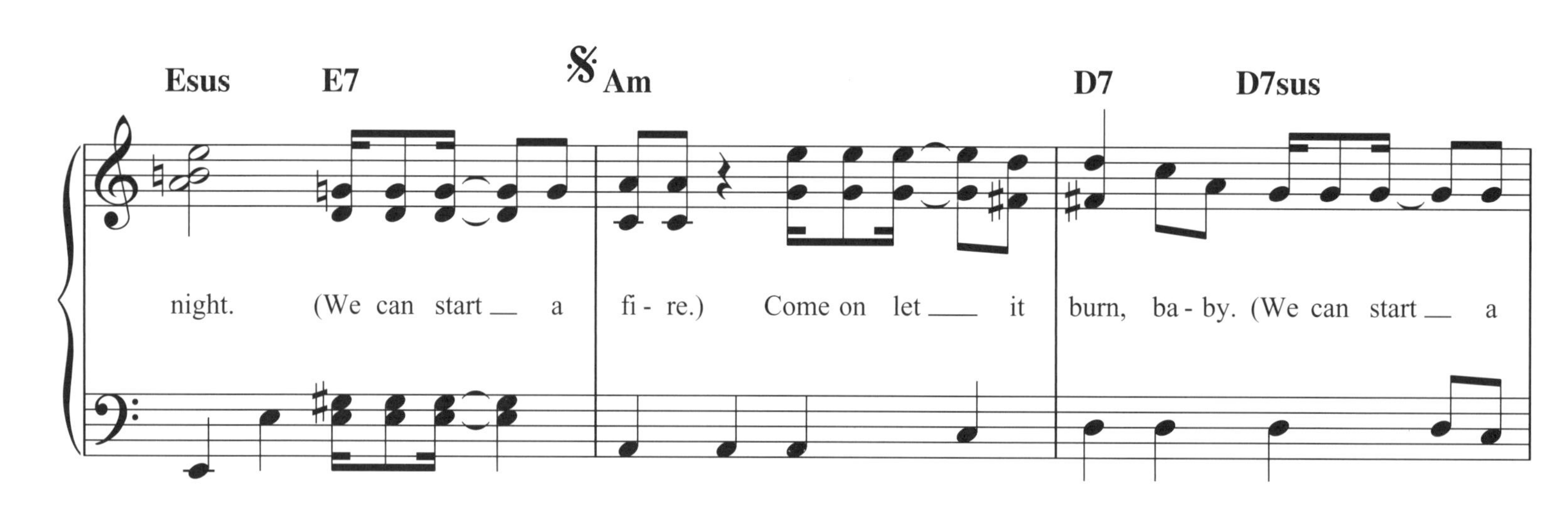
Esus
E7
Am
D7
D7sus
night. (We can start _ a
fi - re.) Come on let ___ it
burn, ba - by. (We can start _ a

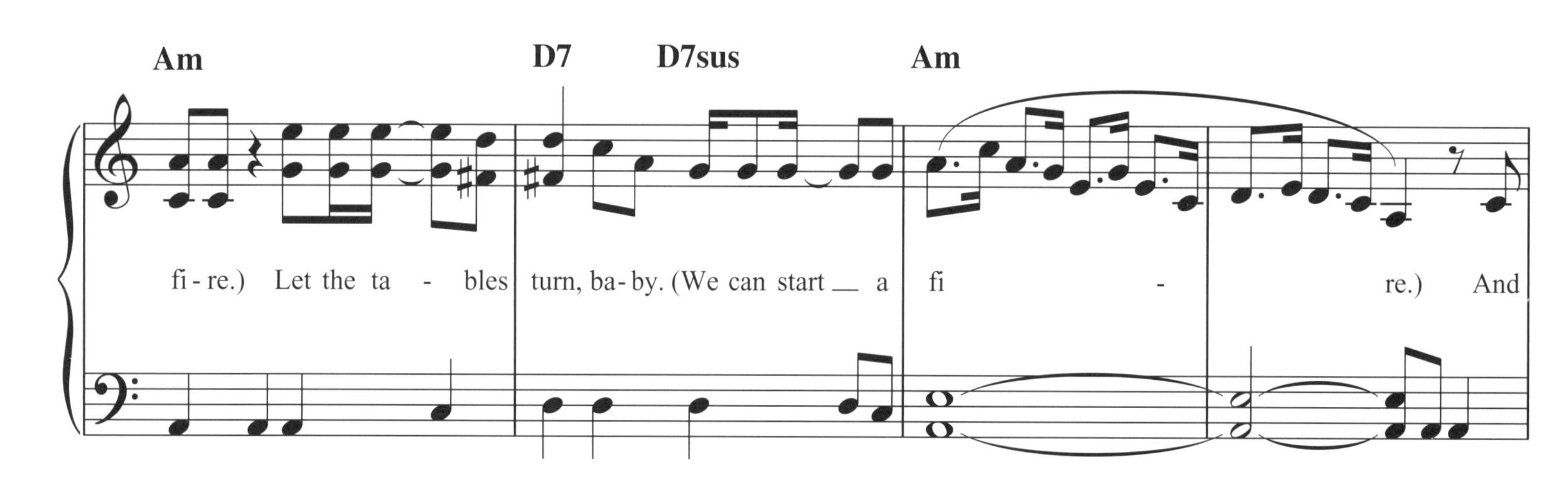
Am
D7
D7sus
Am
fi - re.) Let the ta - bles
turn, ba - by. (We can start _ a
fi - re.) And

F
G
To Coda
F
E7
I just know _ I feel so good,
don't you know _ I feel so good,
I just know _ I feel so good ____

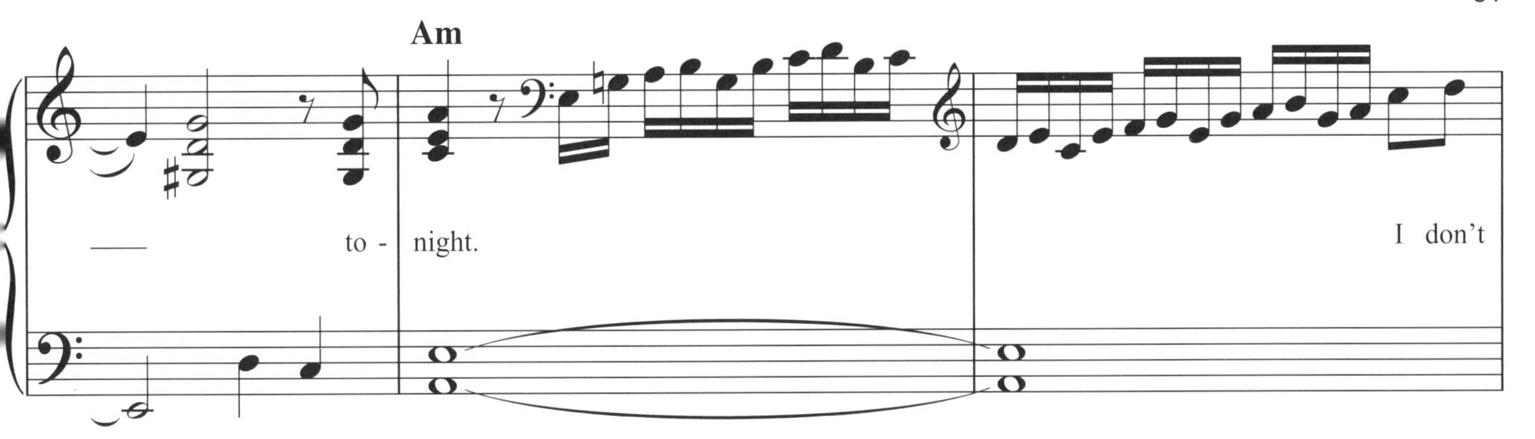
Am
to - night.
I don't

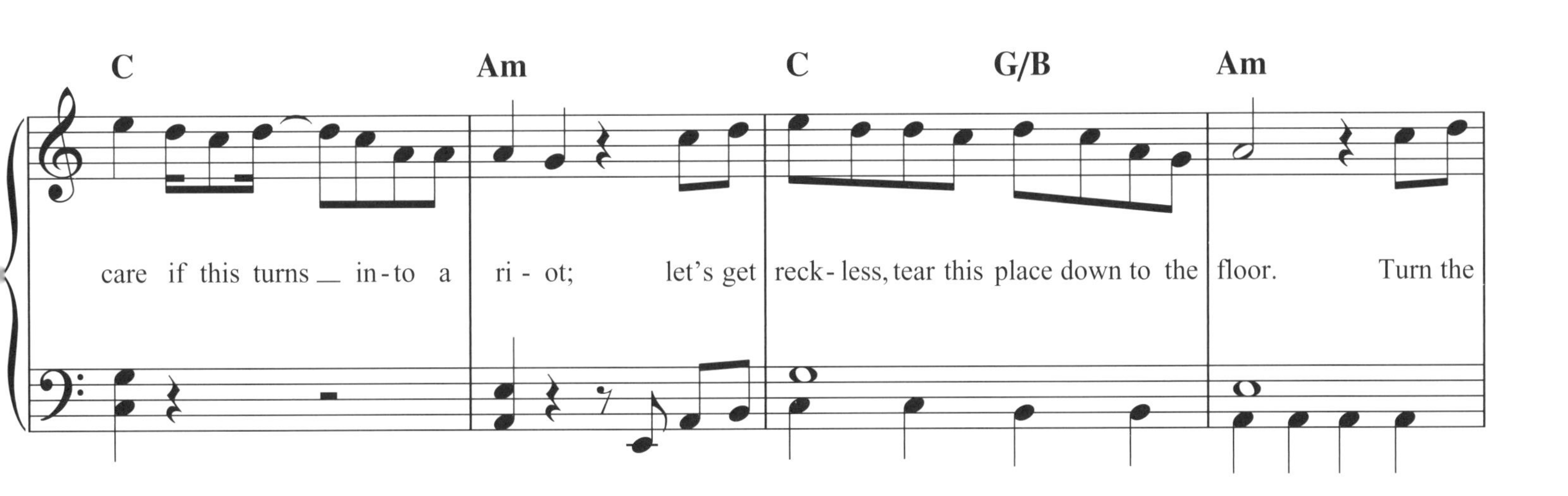
C
Am
C
G/B
Am
care if this turns in-to a ri - ot; let's get reck-less, tear this place down to the floor. Turn the

C
G/B
Am
F/C
G/B
Am
E7
D.S. al Coda
mu-sic way up loud; can't no - bod-y stop us now. Oh, I just know I feel so good to - night. (We can start a

CODA
F
E7♯9
Am
don't you know, don't you know, to - night.

ENGAGEMENT PARTY

Music by
JUSTIN HURWITZ

Moderately slow, expressively

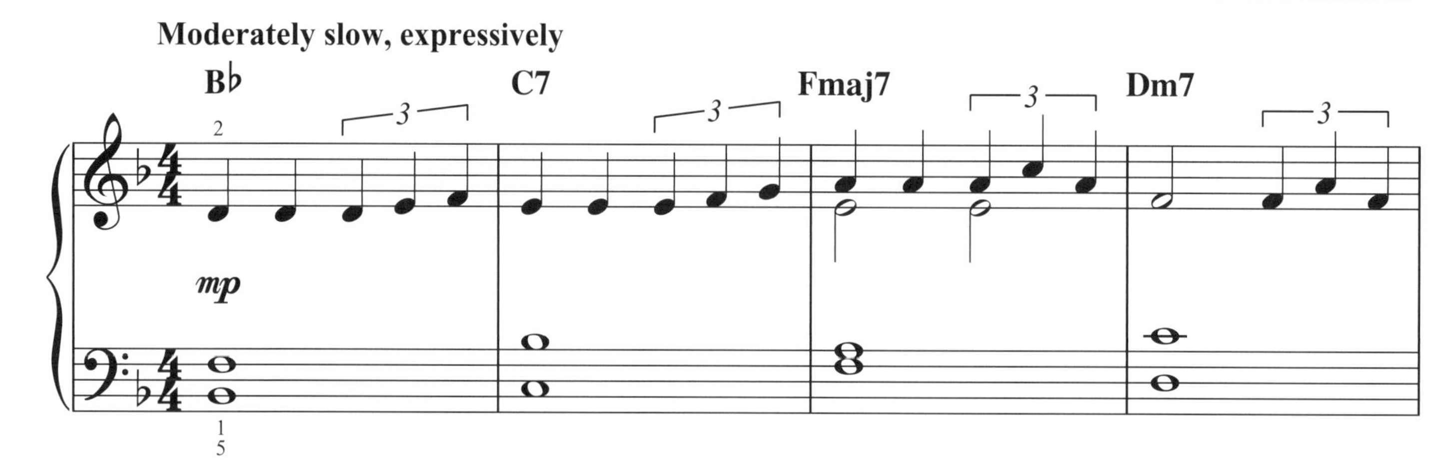

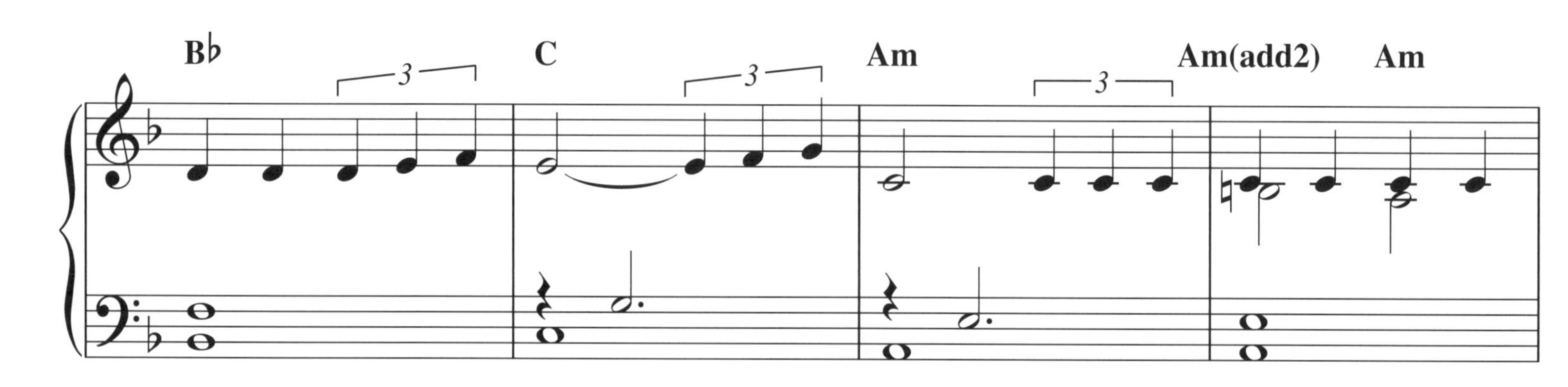

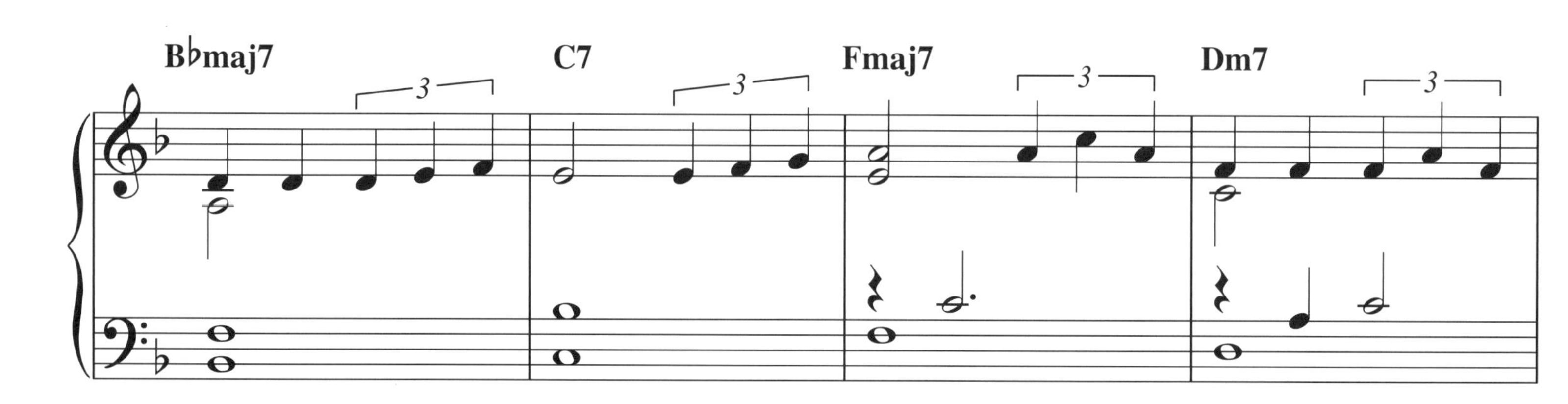

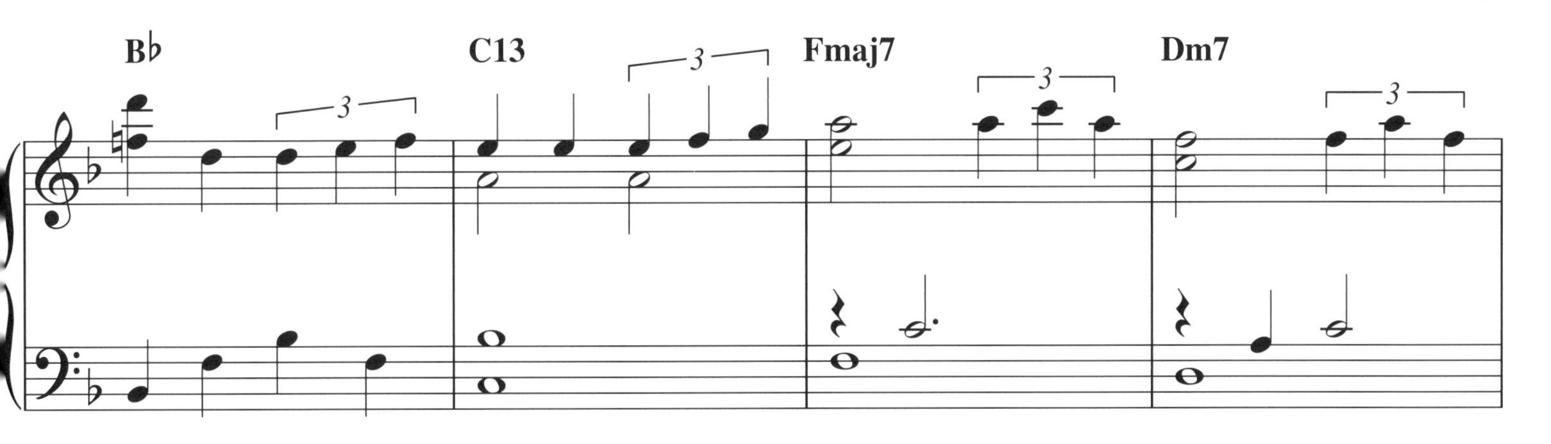
B♭
C13
Fmaj7
Dm7
3

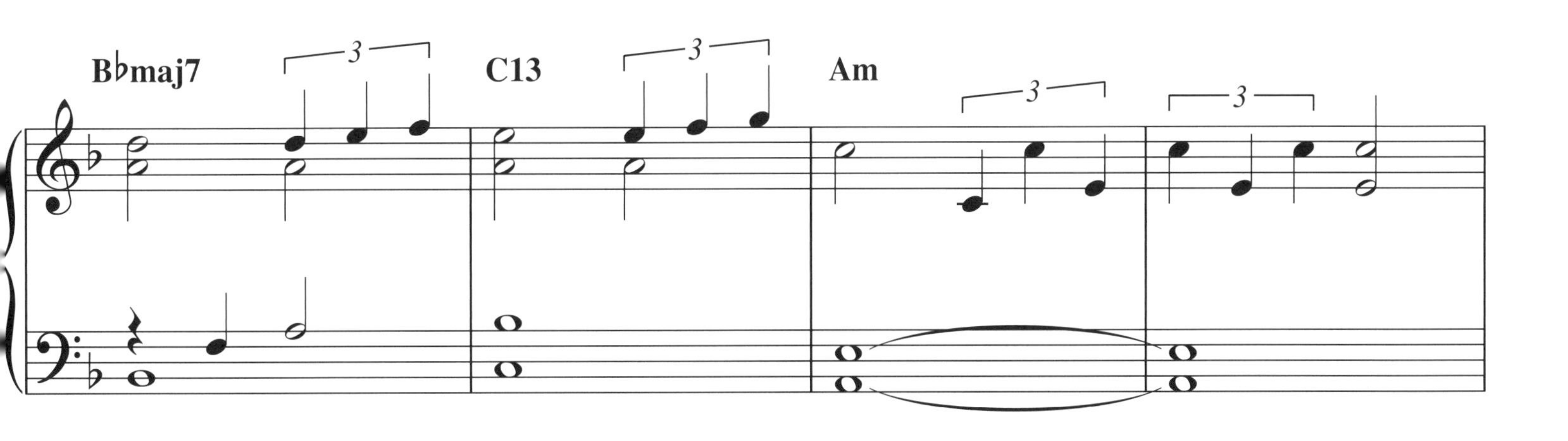
B♭maj7
C13
Am
3

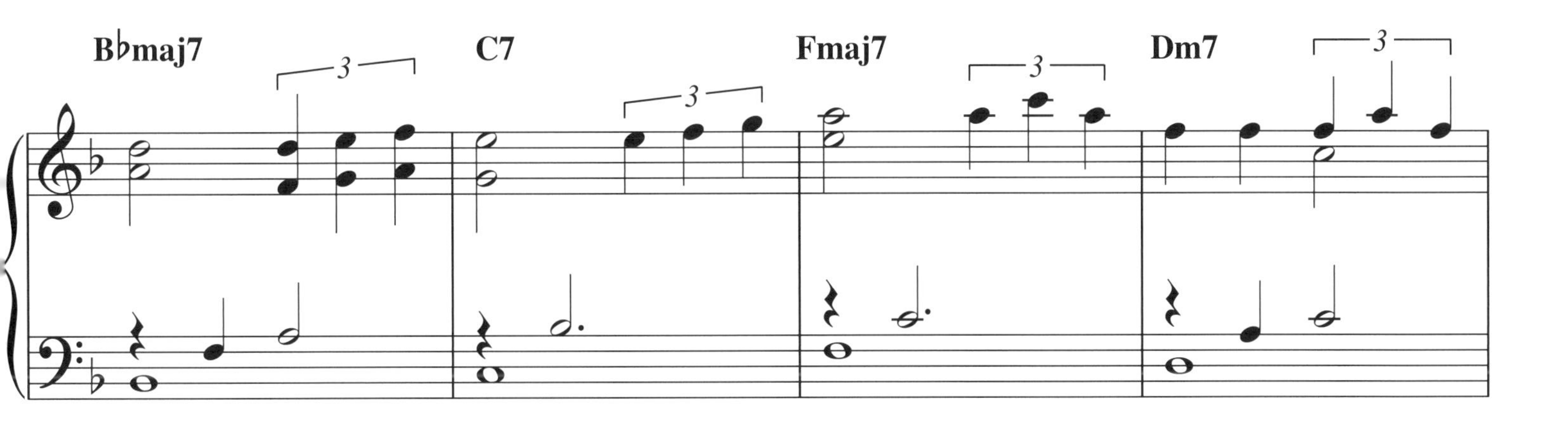
B♭maj7
C7
Fmaj7
Dm7
3

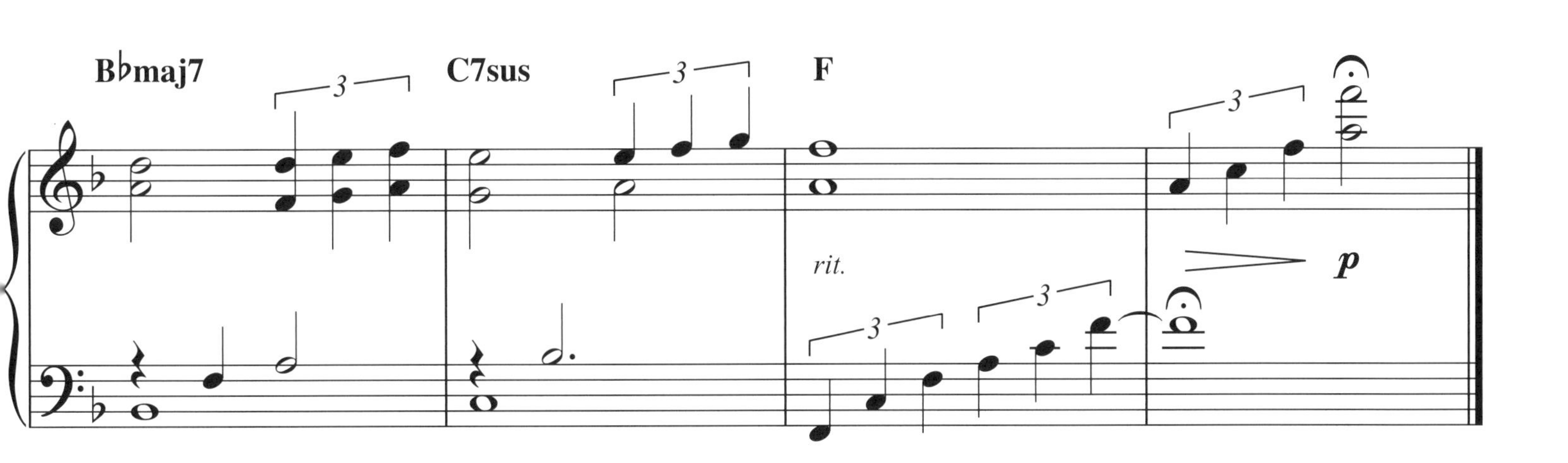
B♭maj7
C7sus
F
3
rit.
p

AUDITION
(The Fools Who Dream)

Music by JUSTIN HURWITZ
Lyrics by BENJ PASEK & JUSTIN PAUL

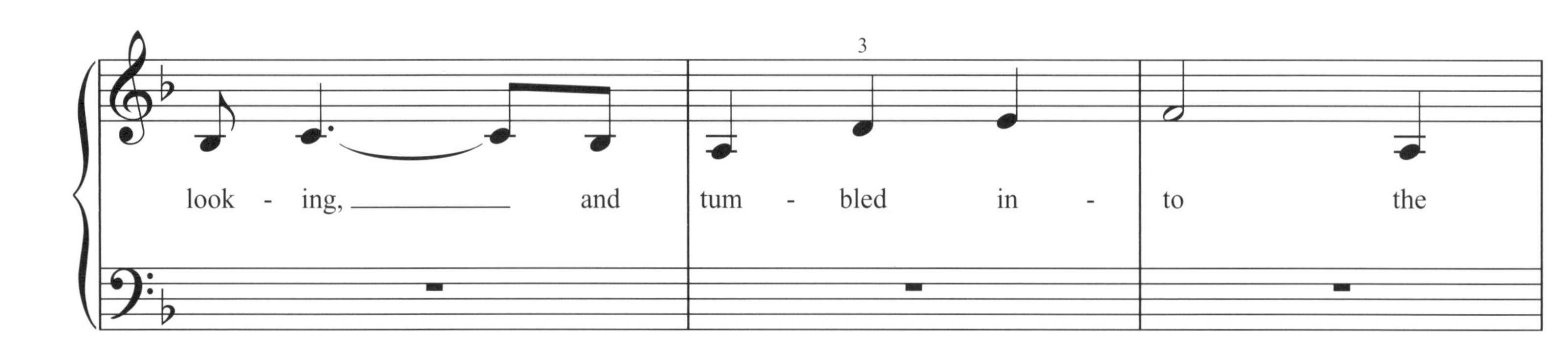

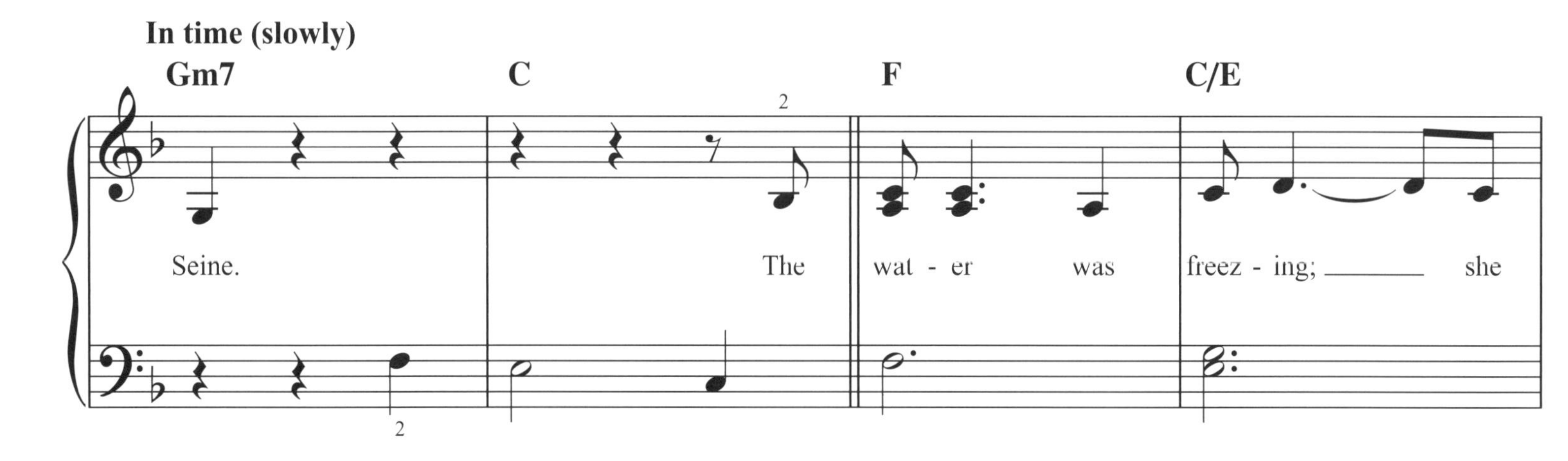

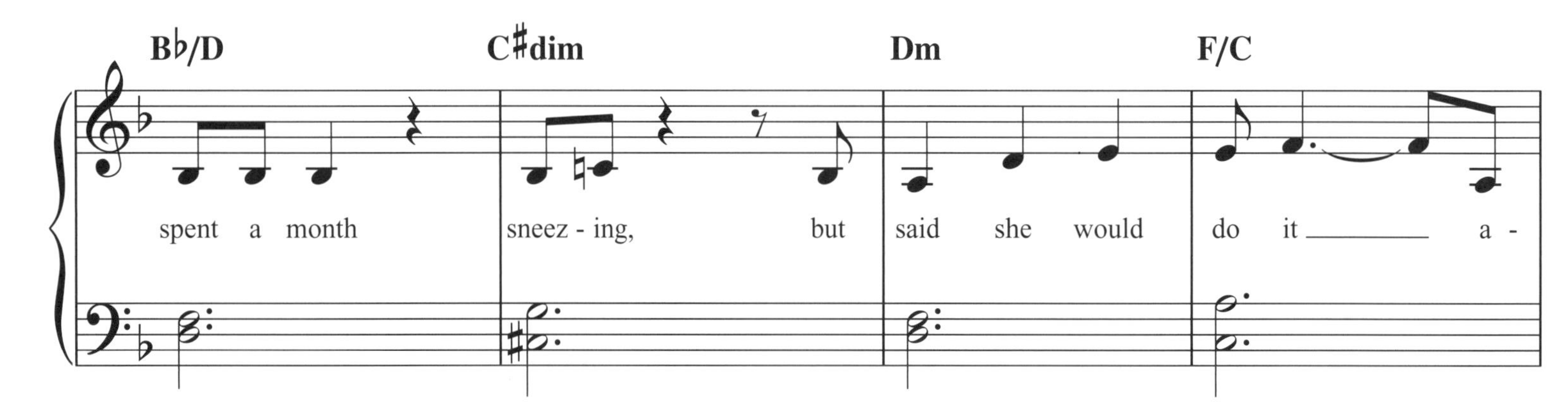

Gm/B♭
C/E
Gm7
C7
gain.
Here's to the ones who

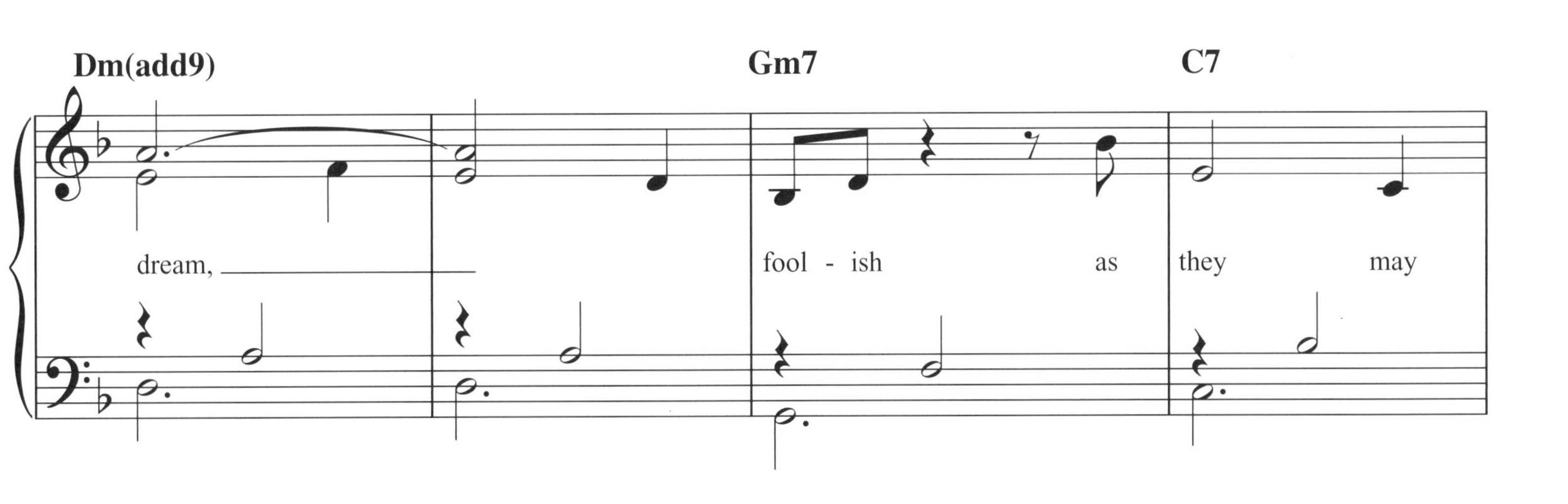
Dm(add9)
Gm7
C7
dream,
fool - ish as they may

Fmaj7
F6
Gm7
C7
seem.
Here's to the hearts that

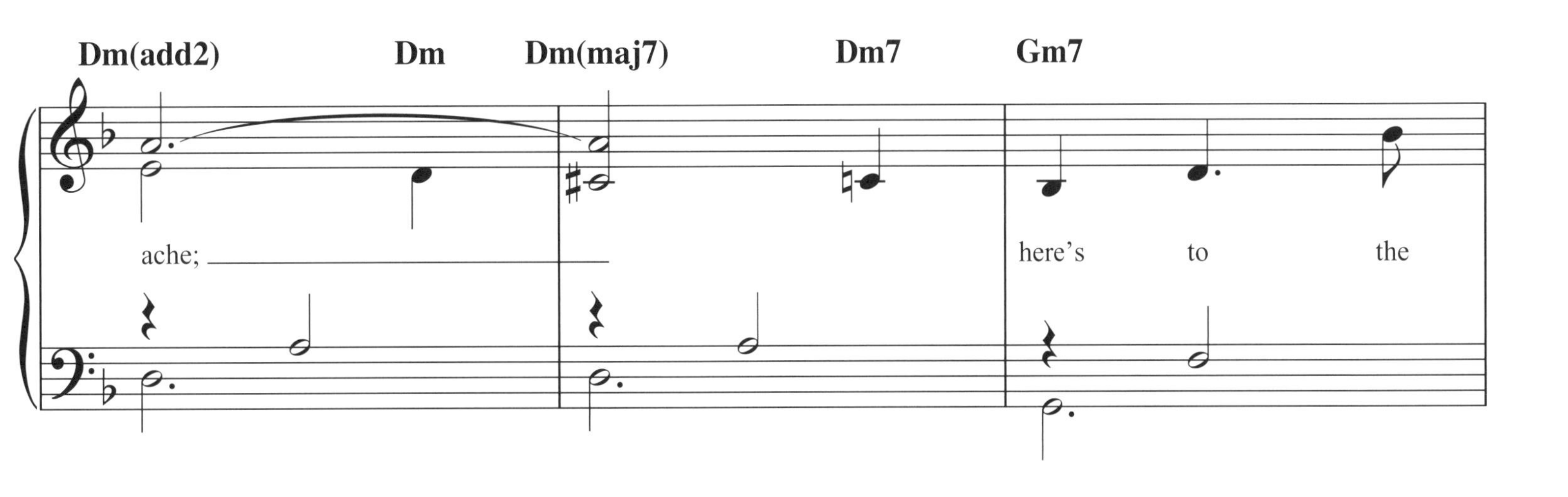
Dm(add2)
Dm
Dm(maj7)
Dm7
Gm7
ache;
here's to the

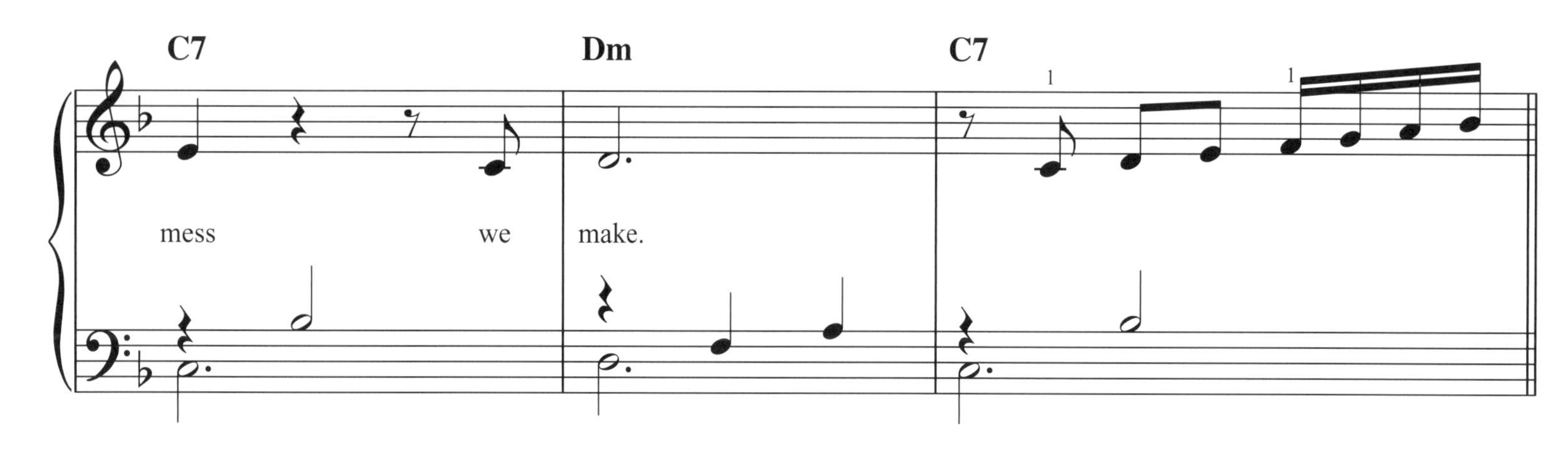
C7
Dm
C7
mess
we
make.

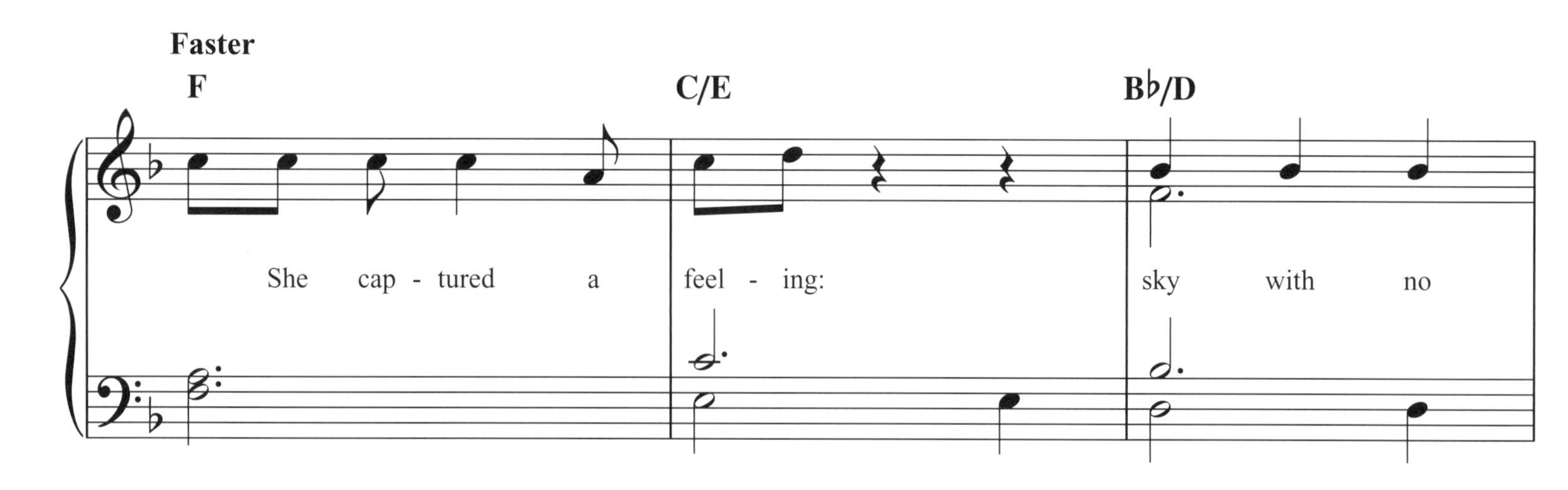
Faster
F
C/E
B♭/D
She cap - tured a
feel - ing:
sky with no

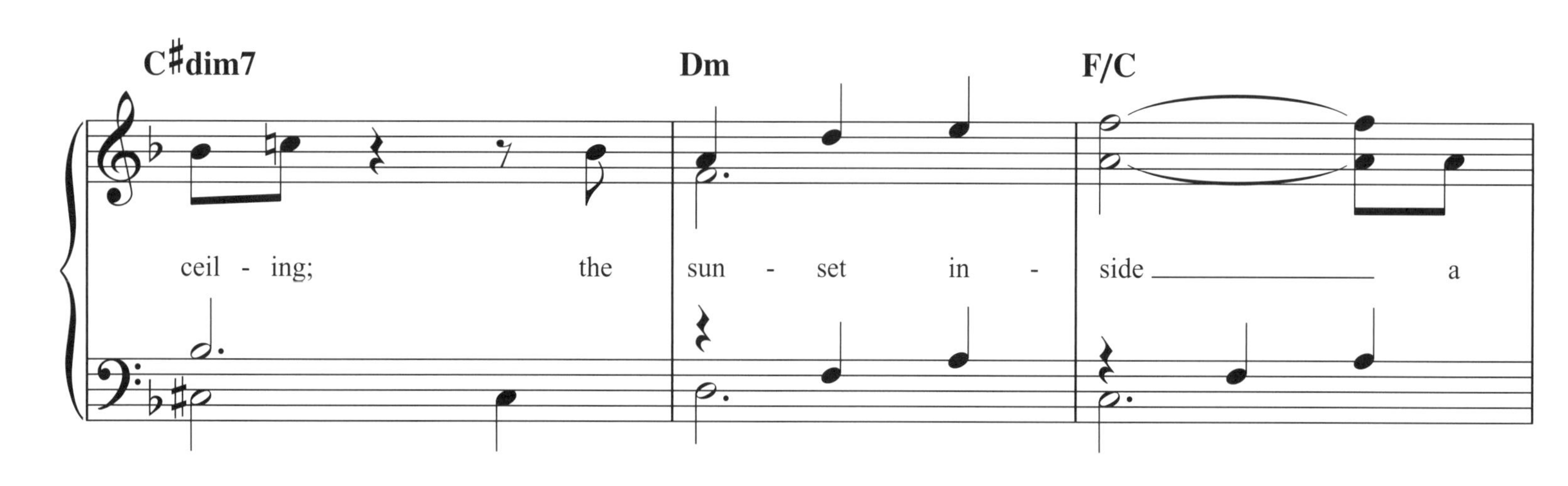
C♯dim7
Dm
F/C
ceil - ing;
the
sun - set in -
side
a

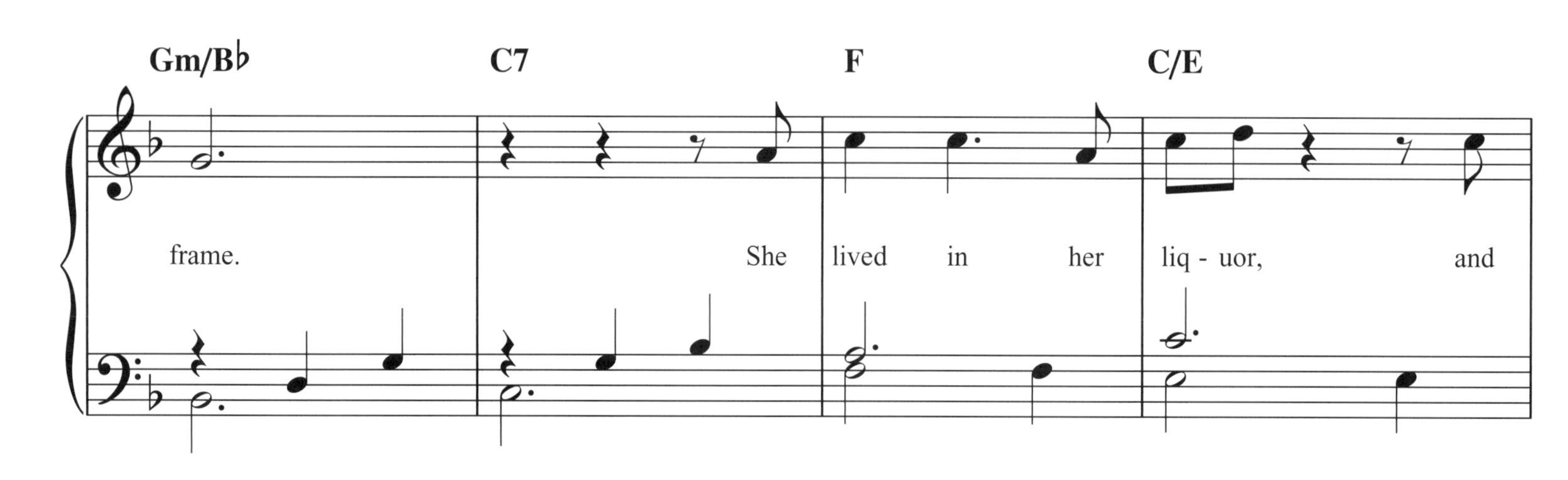
Gm/B♭
C7
F
C/E
frame.
She
lived in her
liq - uor,
and

B♭/D
C♯dim7
Dm
F/C
died with a flick - er; I'll al - ways re - mem - ber the

Gm/B♭
C
Gm7
C7
flame. Here's to the ones who

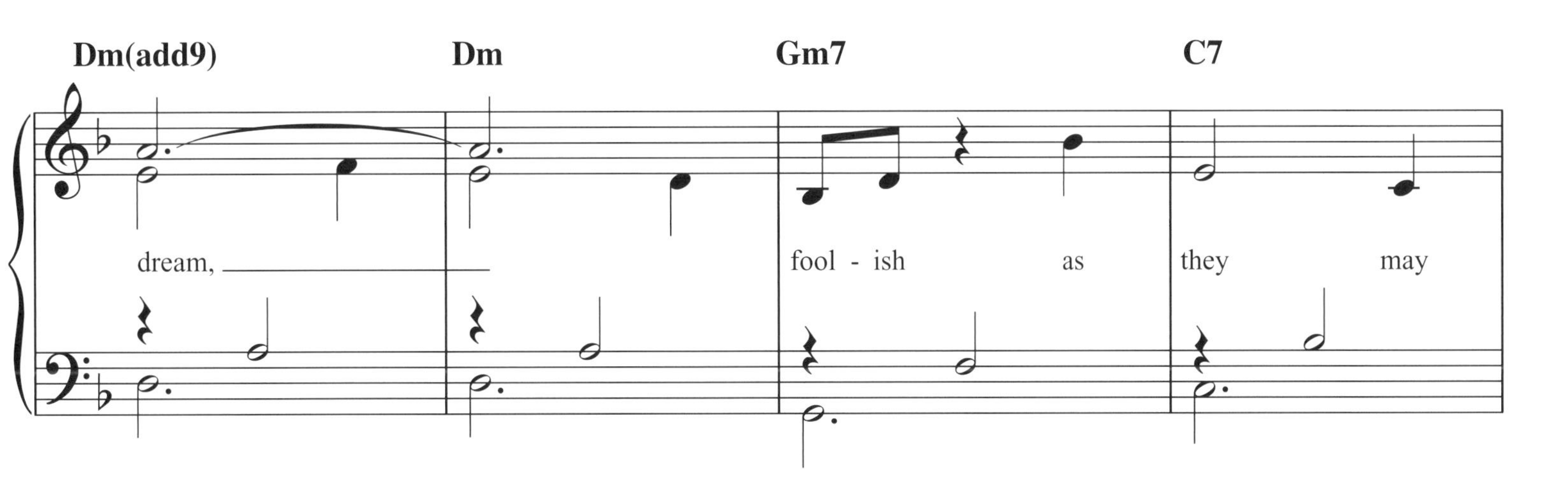
Dm(add9)
Dm
Gm7
C7
dream, fool - ish as they may

Fmaj7
F6
Gm7
C7
seem. Here's to the hearts that

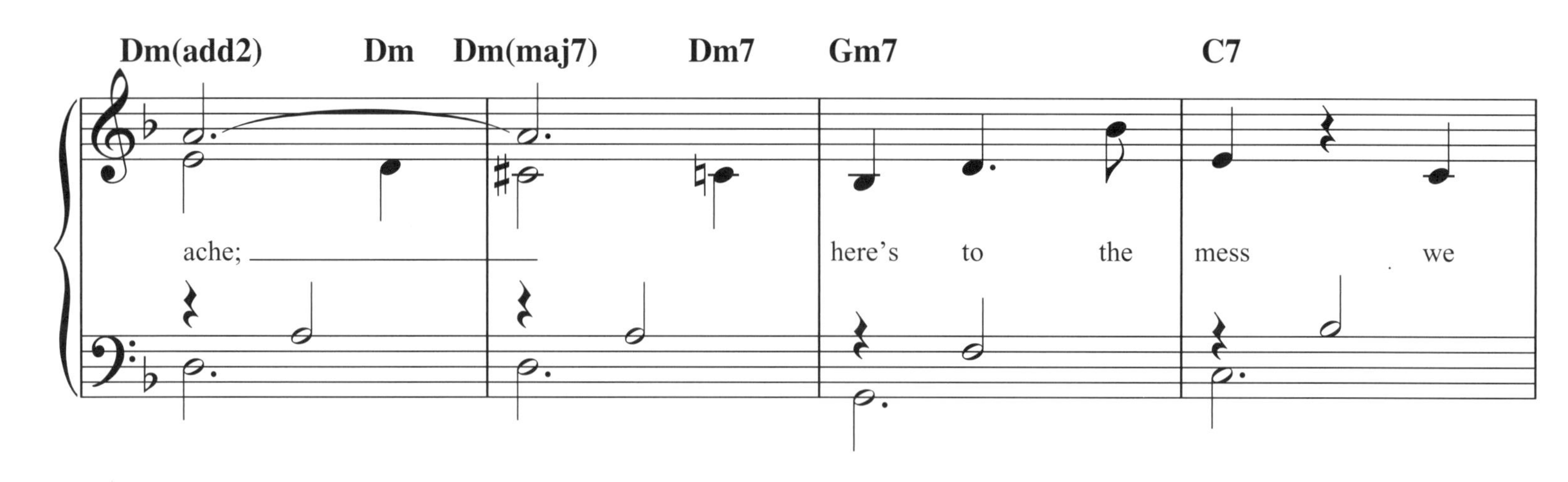
Dm(add2) Dm Dm(maj7) Dm7 Gm7 C7
ache; here's to the mess we

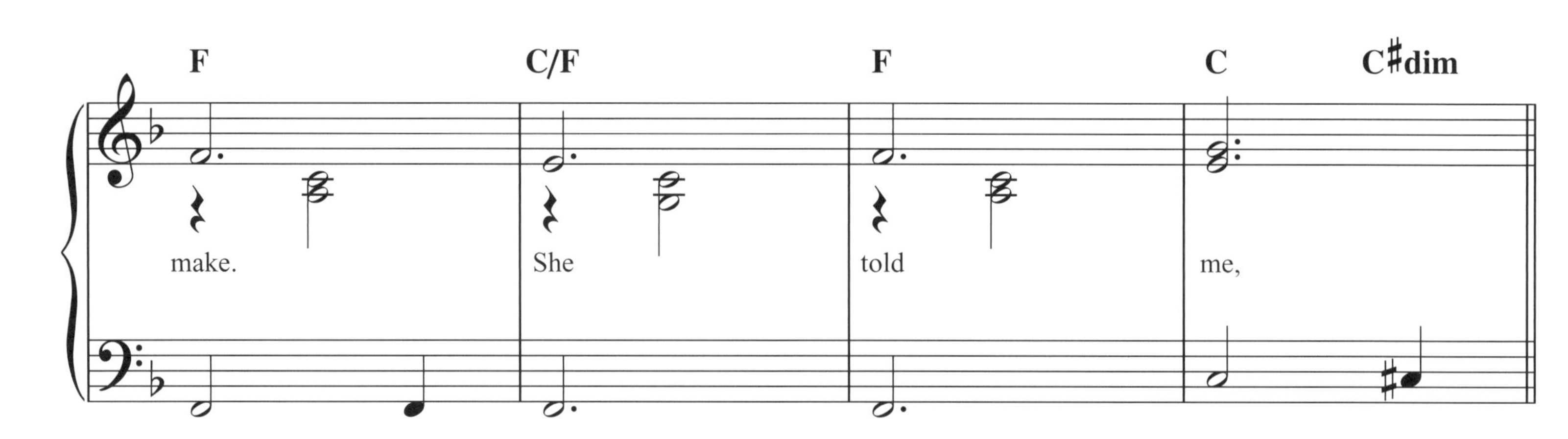
F C/F F C C♯dim
make. She told me,

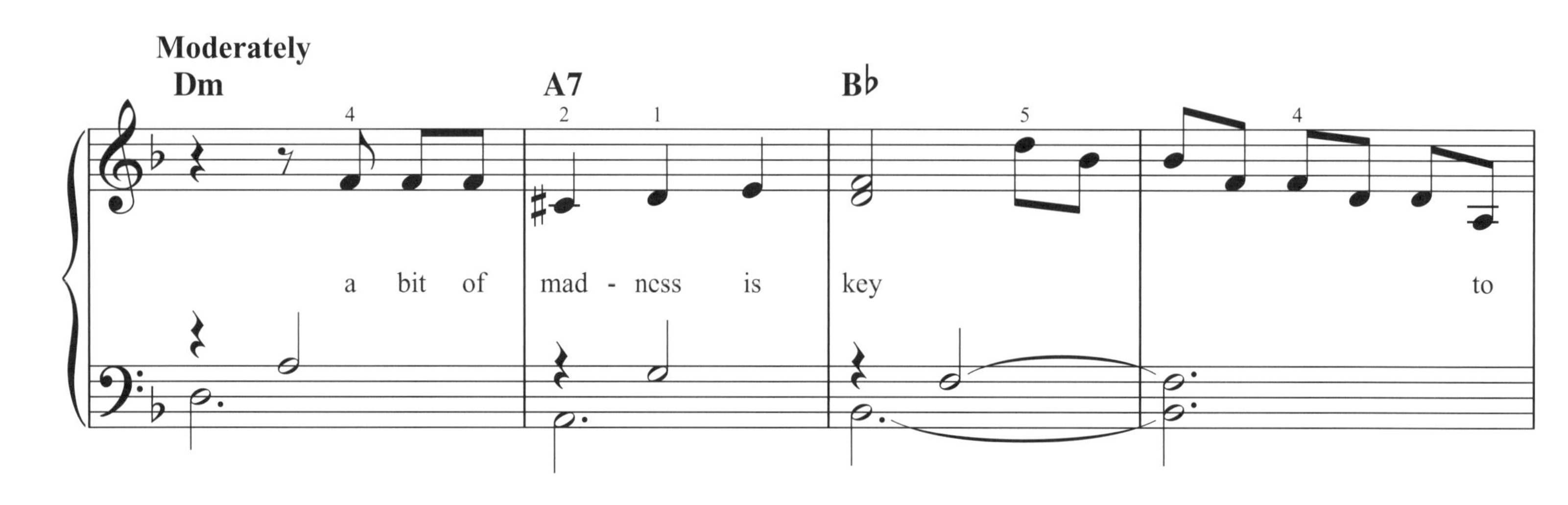
Moderately
Dm A7 B♭
a bit of mad - ness is key to

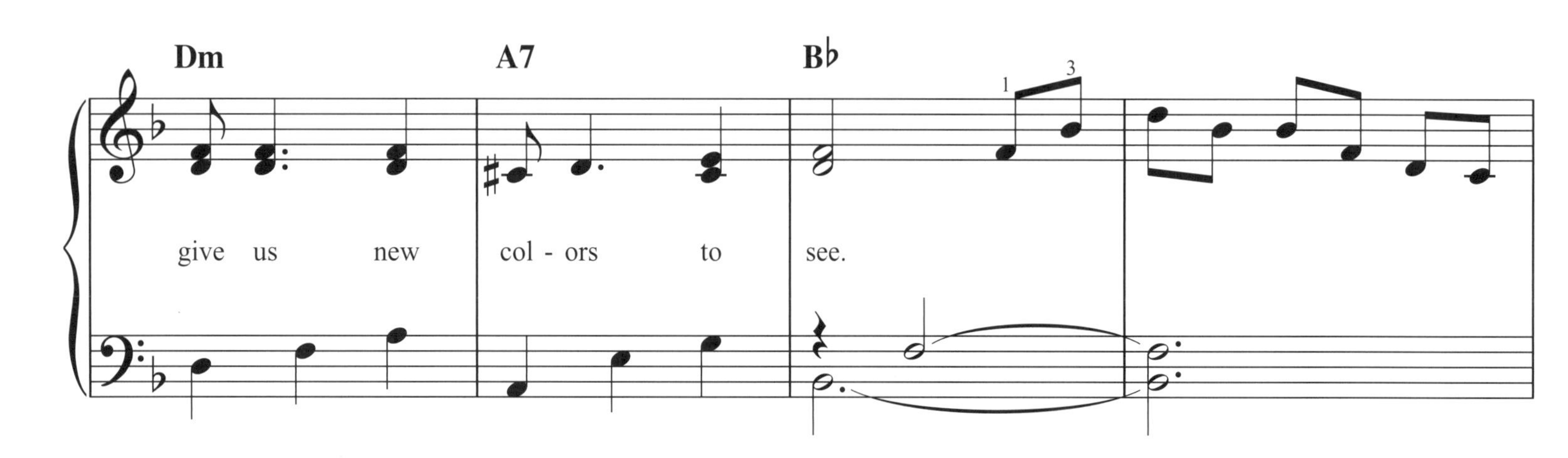
Dm A7 B♭
give us new col - ors to see.

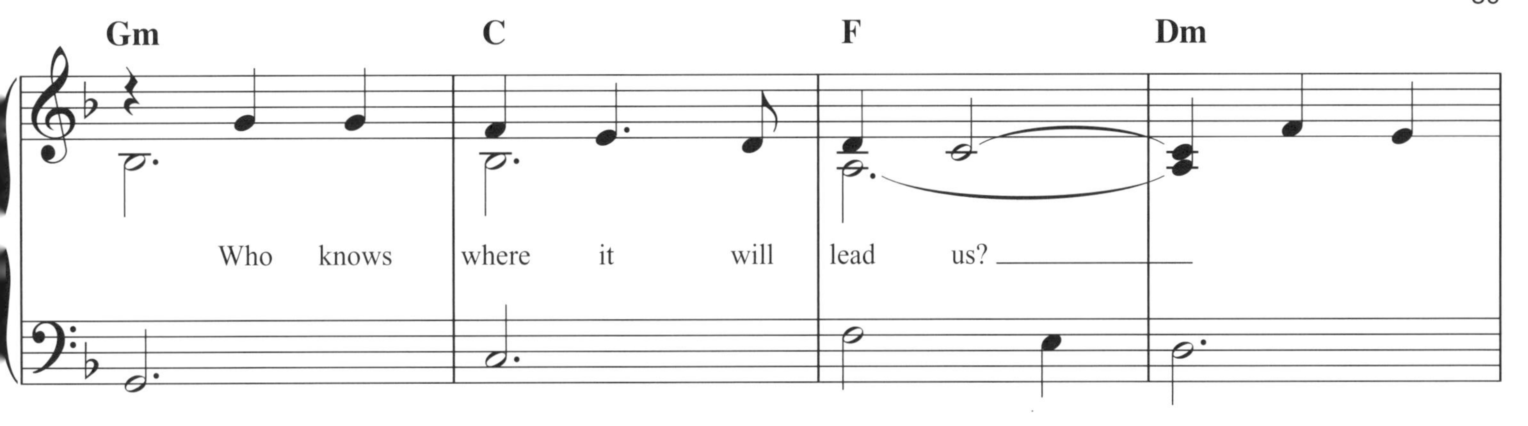
Gm
C
F
Dm
Who knows where it will lead us?

Gm
C7
F
Am7
D
And that's why they need us.
So,

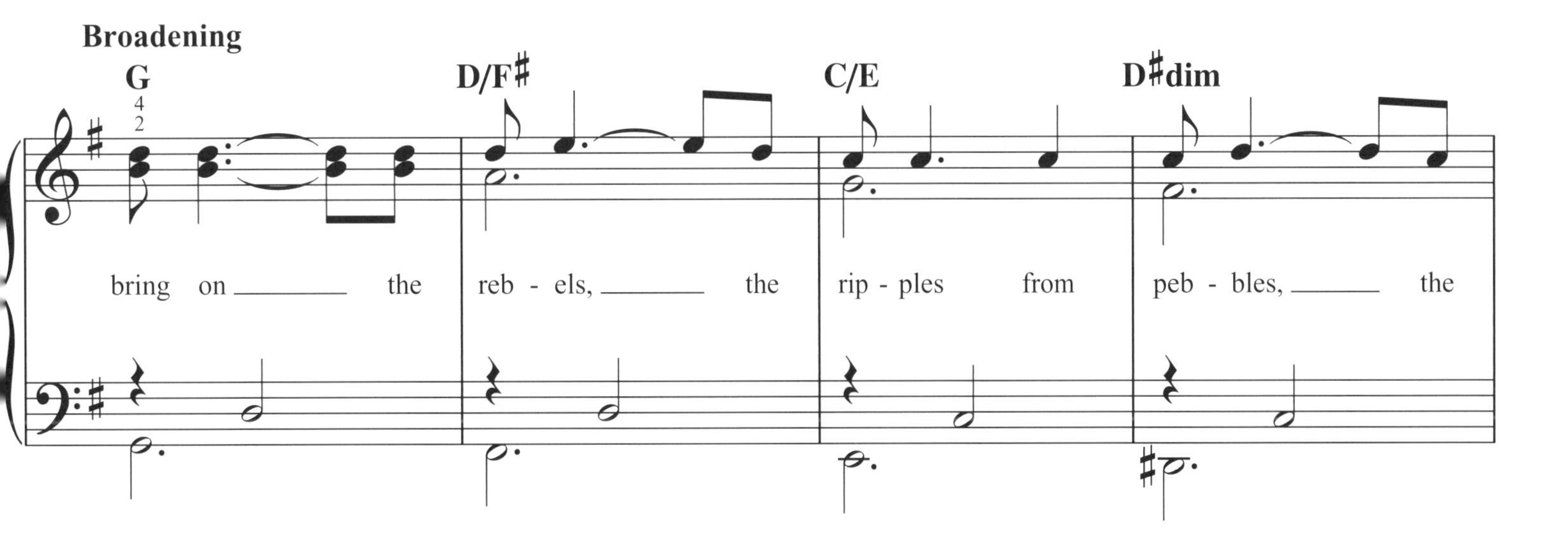
Broadening
G
D/F♯
C/E
D♯dim
bring on the reb - els, the rip - ples from peb - bles, the

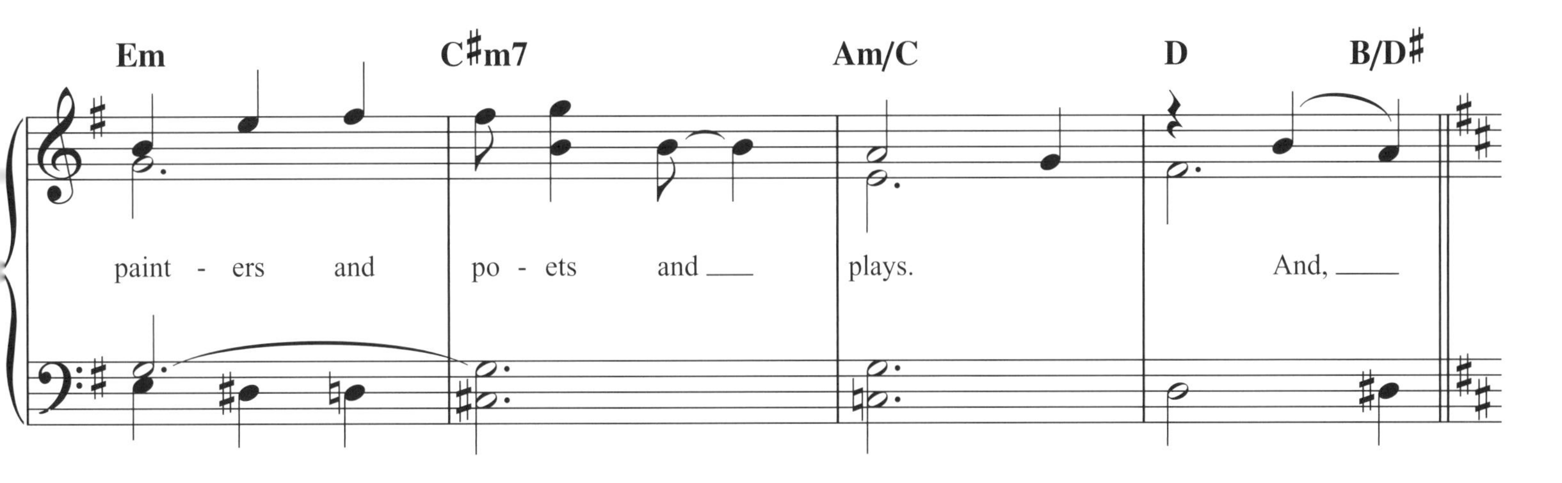
Em
C♯m7
Am/C
D
B/D♯
paint - ers and po - ets and plays.
And,

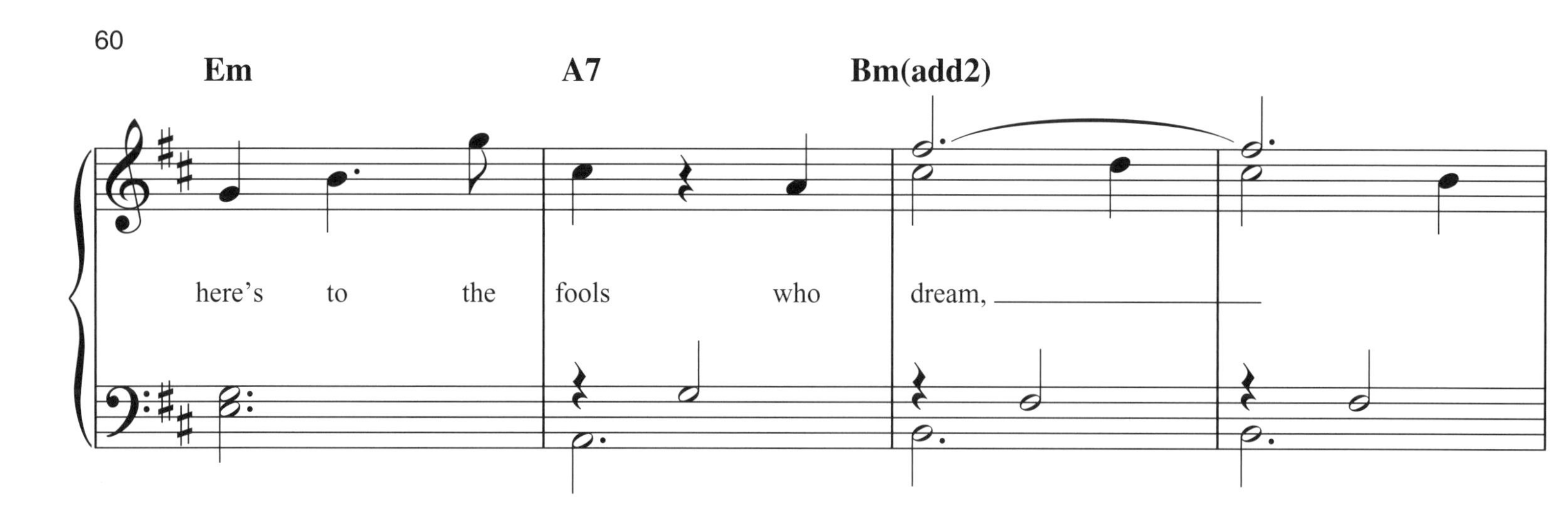
Em
A7
Bm(add2)
here's to the fools who dream,

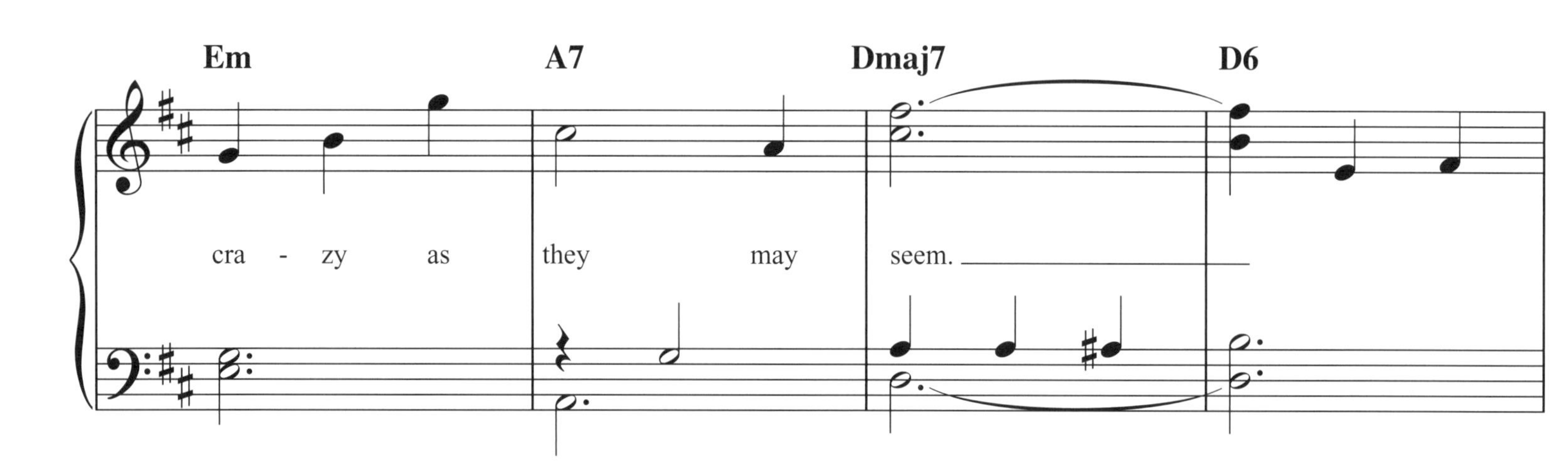
Em
A7
Dmaj7
D6
cra - zy as they may seem.

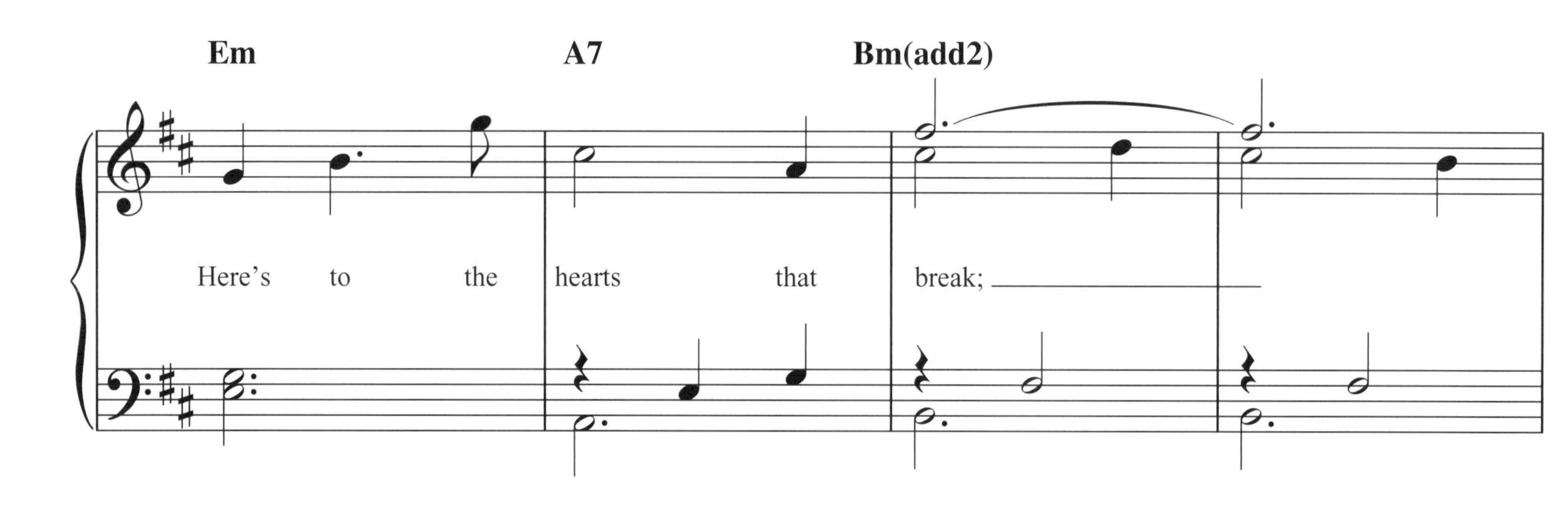
Em
A7
Bm(add2)
Here's to the hearts that break;

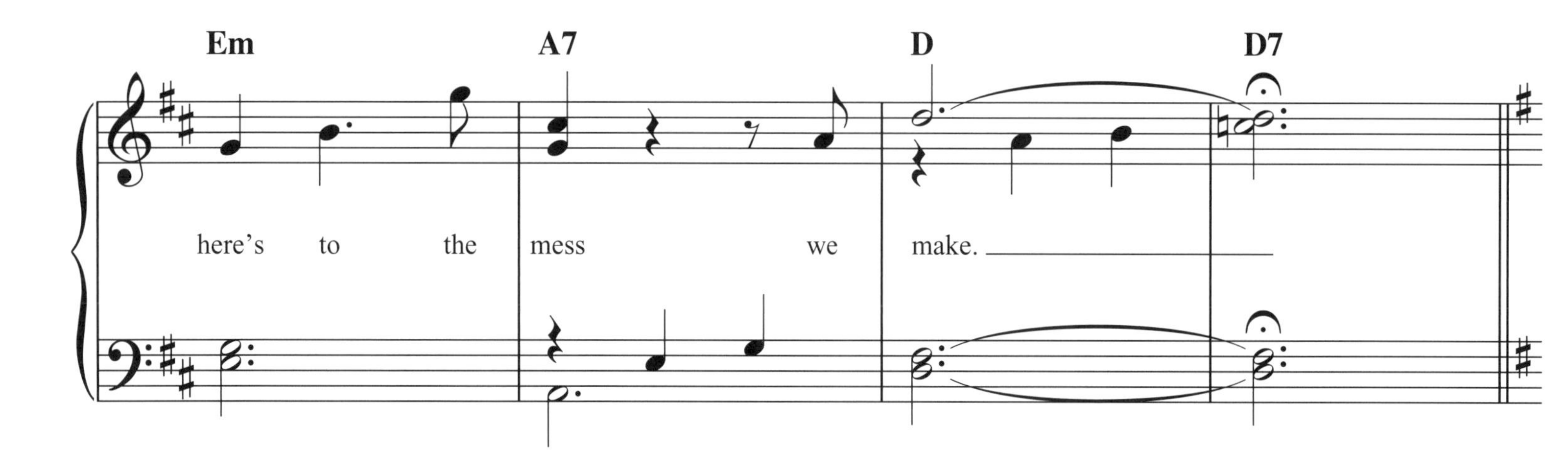
Em
A7
D
D7
here's to the mess we make.

Slower, with freedom

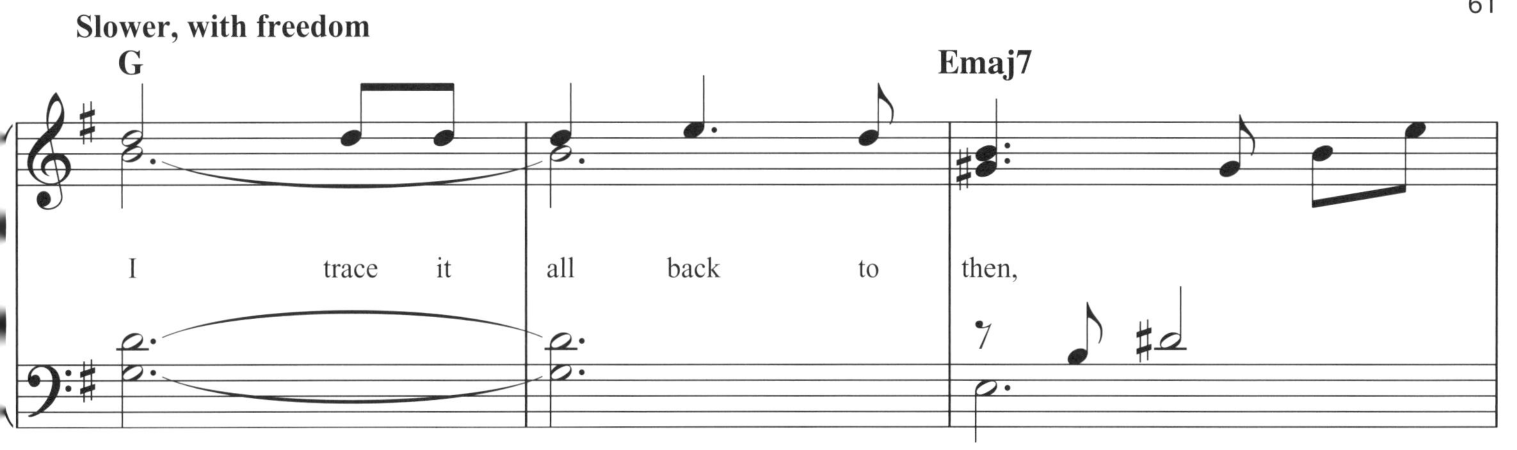

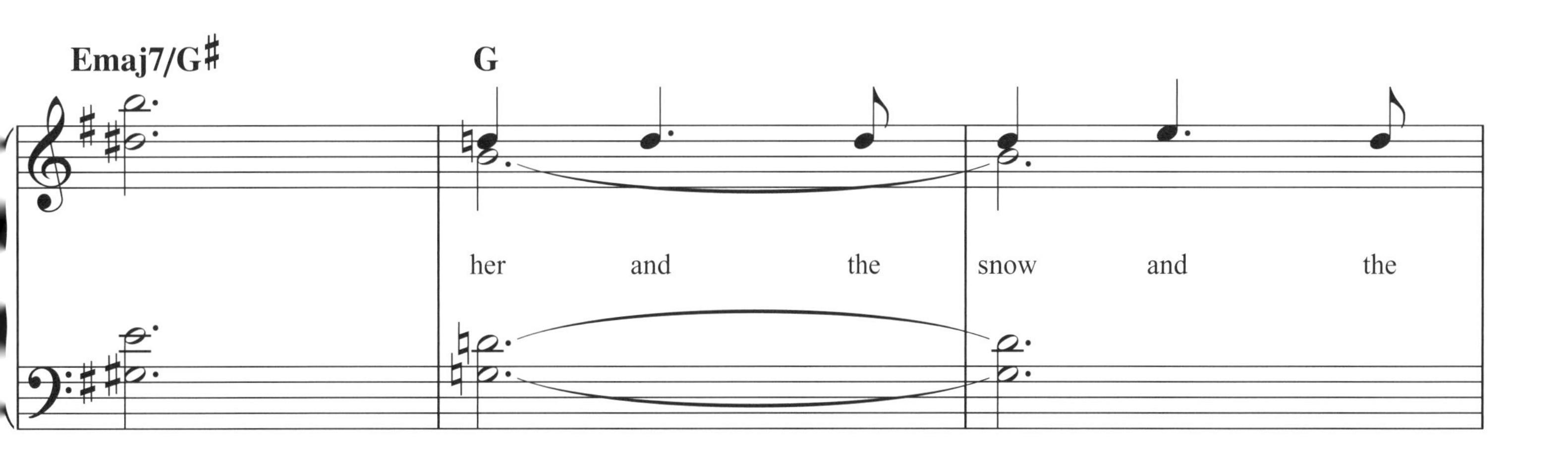

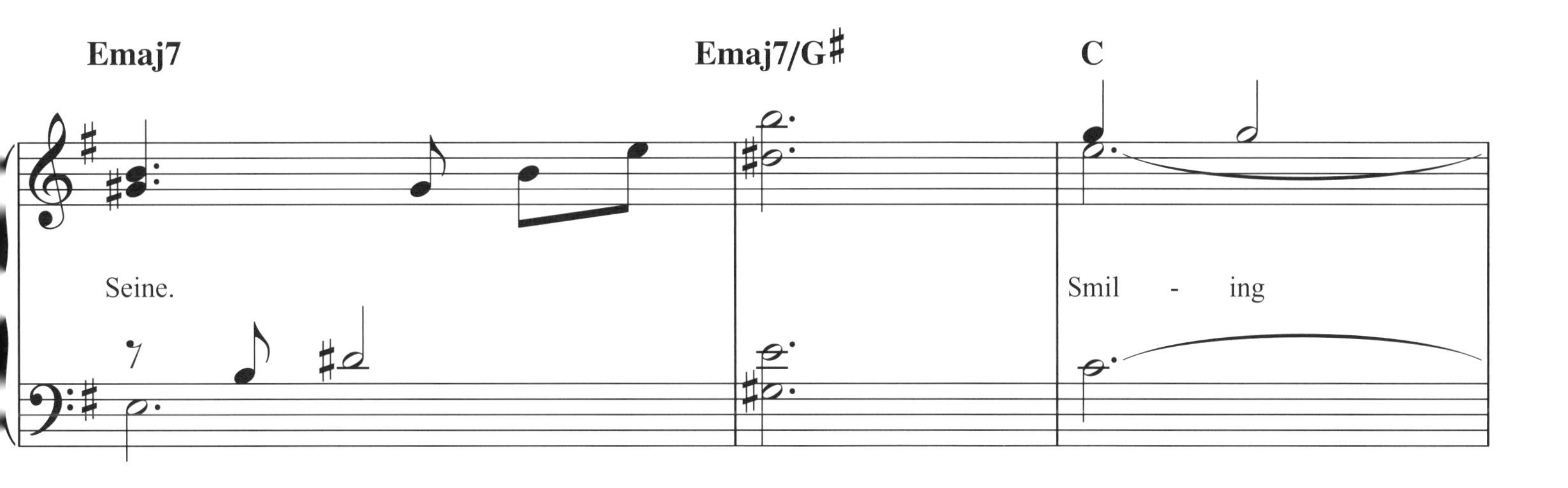

EPILOGUE

Music by
JUSTIN HURWITZ

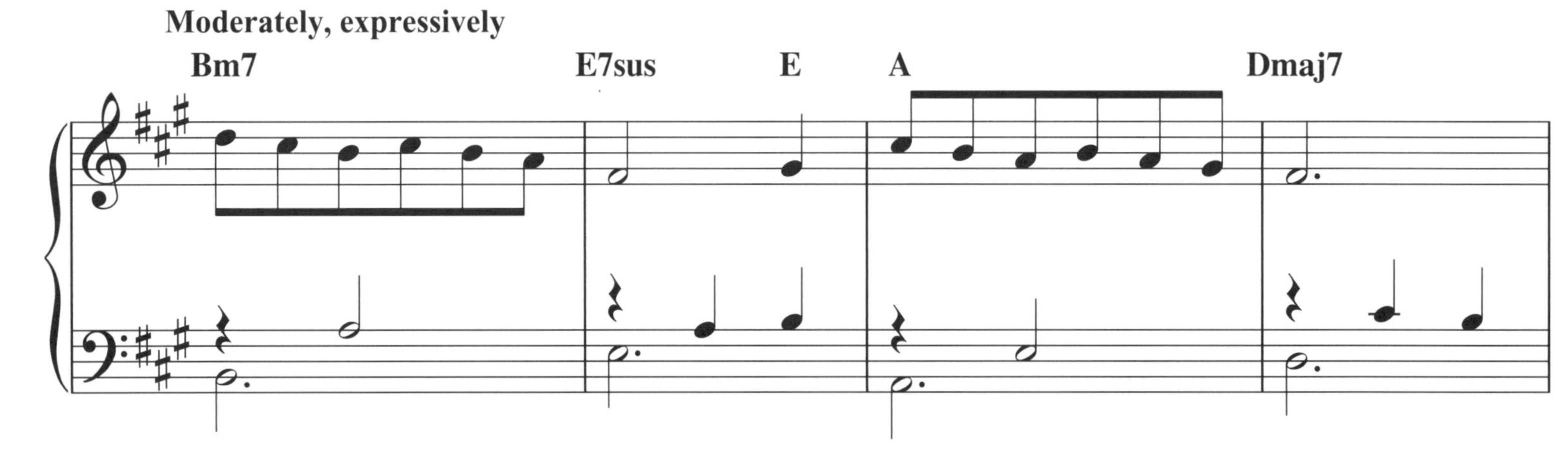

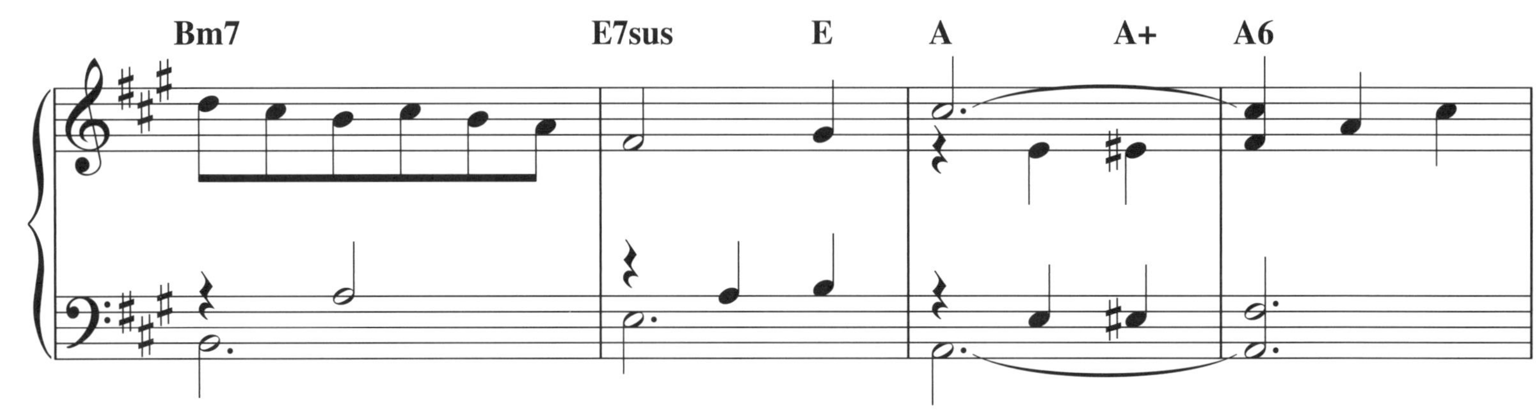

Bm7
E
C♯7♭9
F♯m

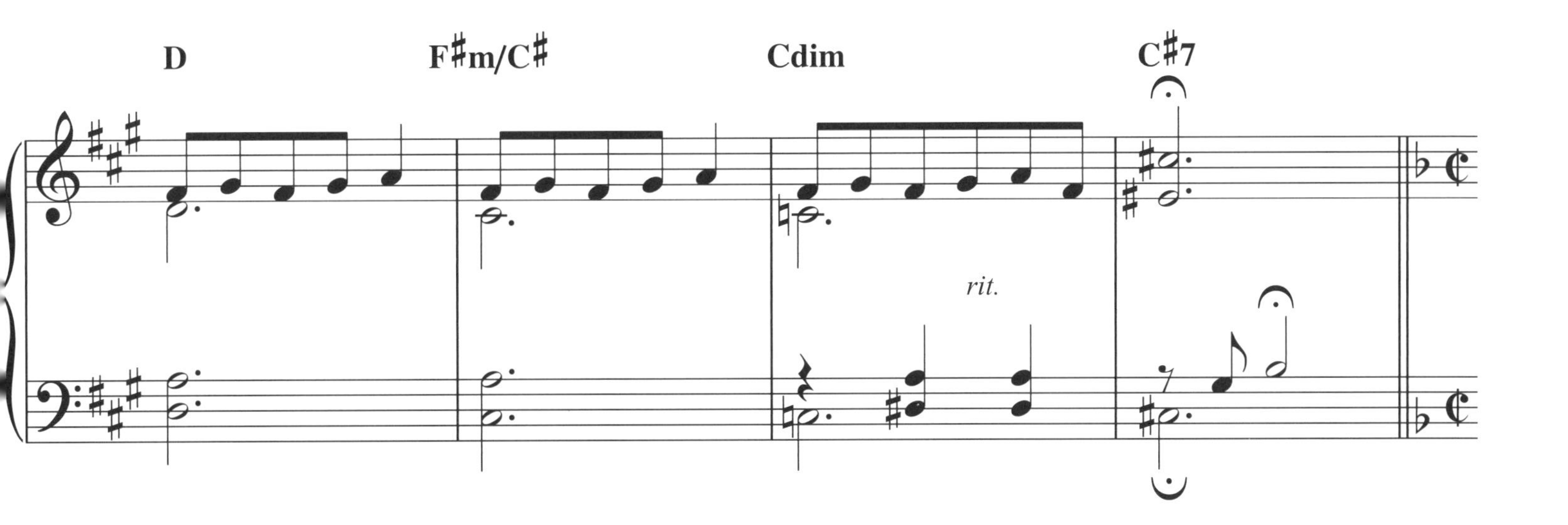
D
F♯m/C♯
Cdim
C♯7
rit.

Moderately fast, in 2
B♭
C7
mf

F
Am

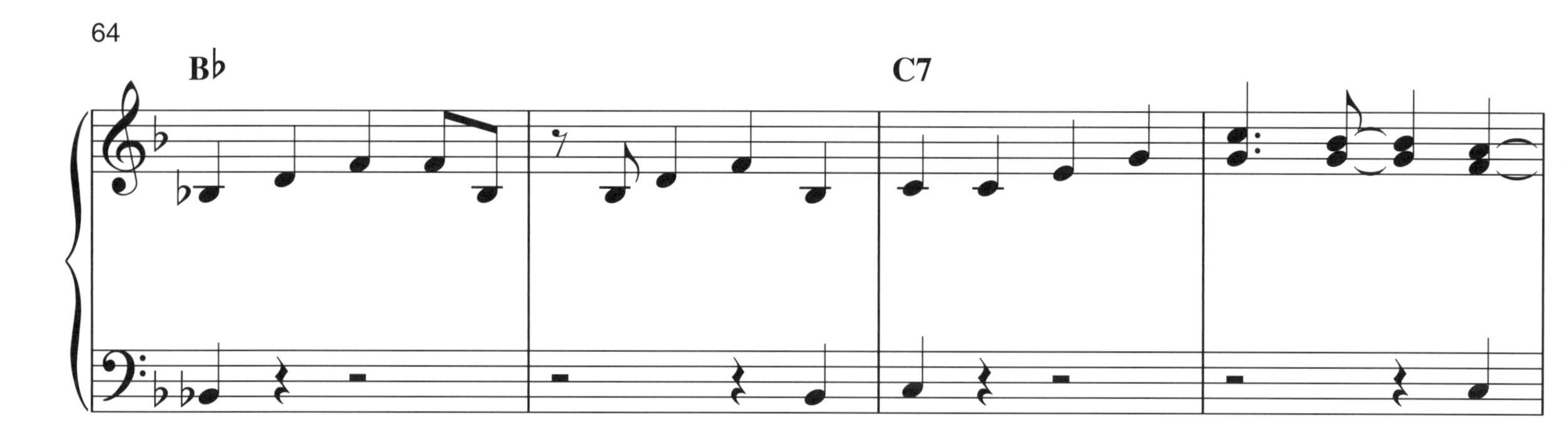
B♭
C7

Dm
B♭
Am

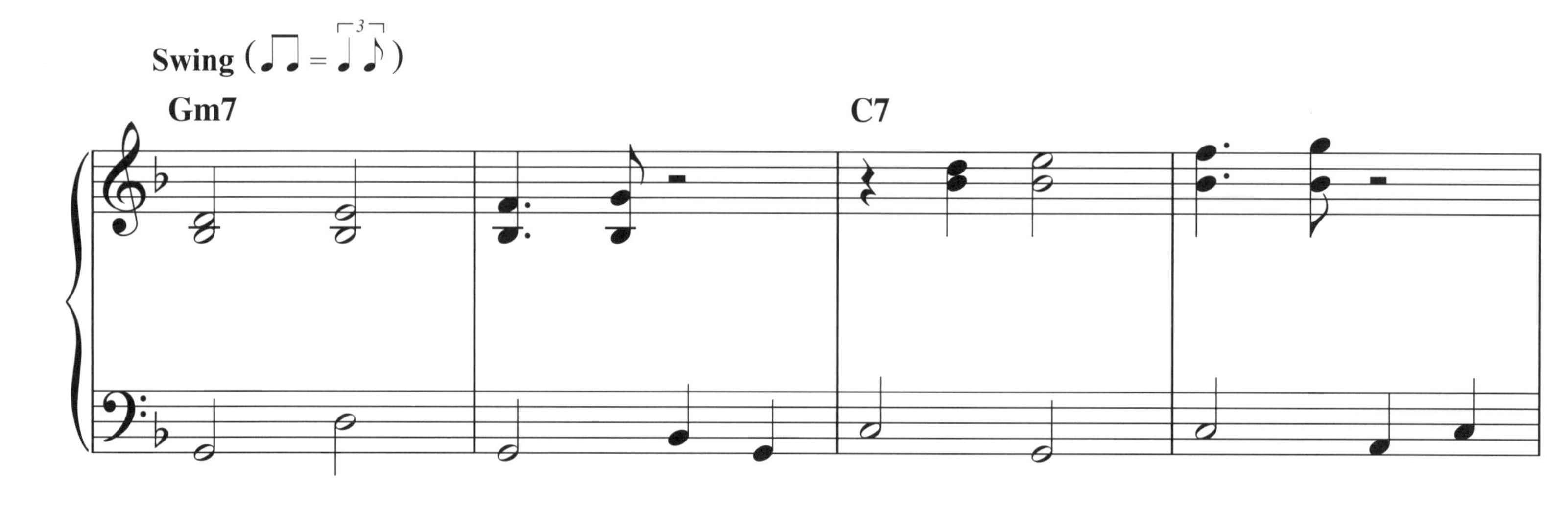
Swing
3
Gm7
C7

Dm
B♭
Am

Gm7
C7

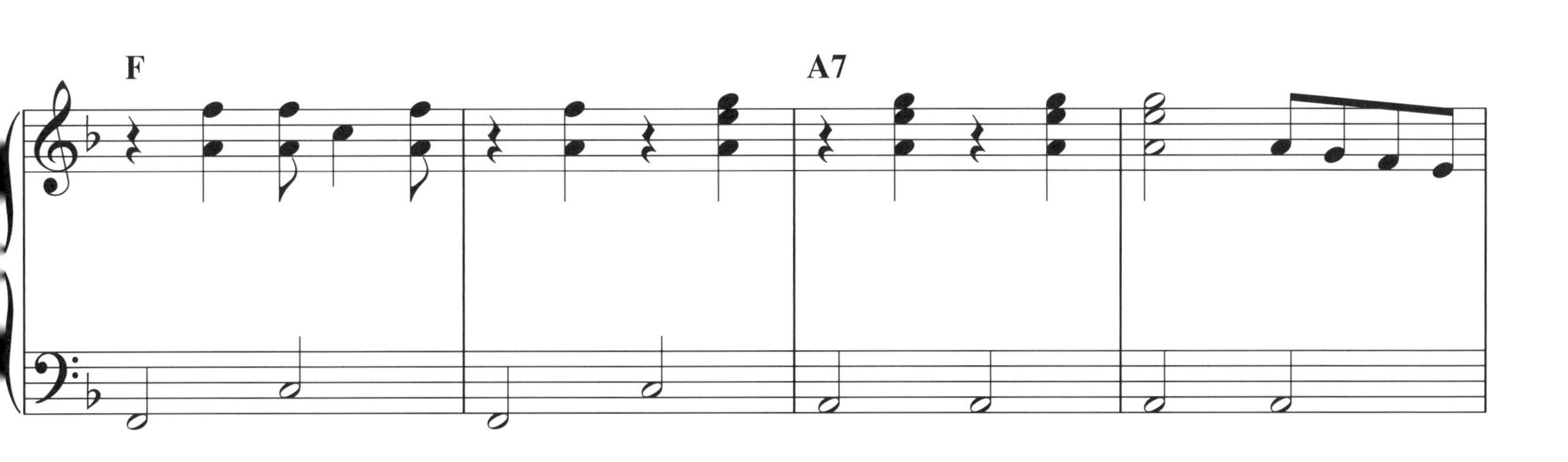

F
A7

B♭maj7
C7
F

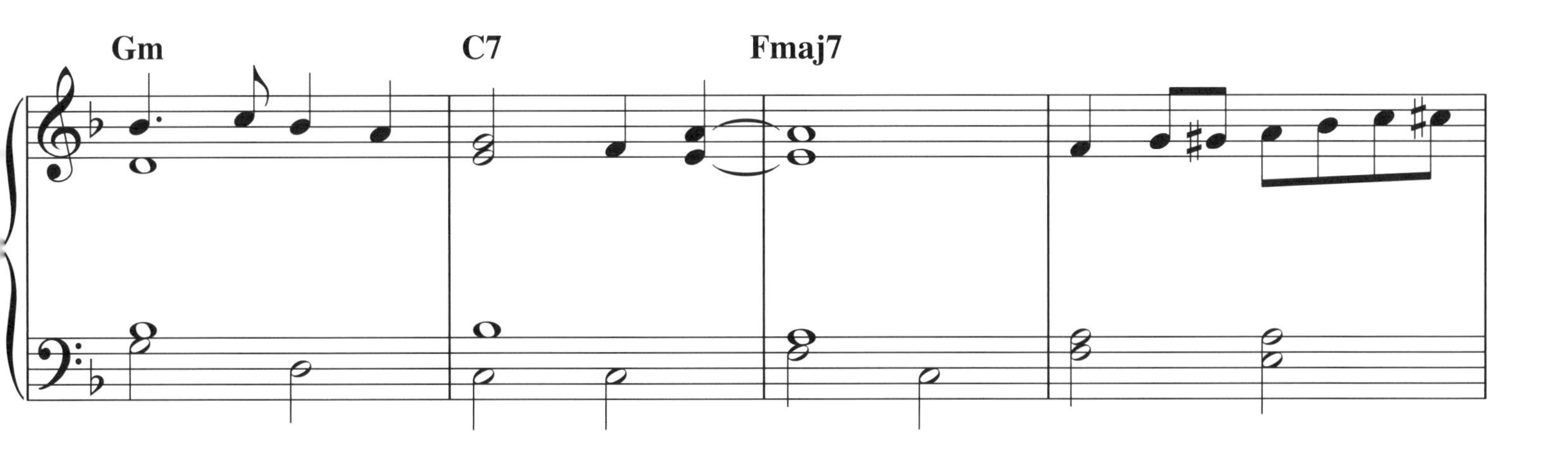

Gm
C7
Fmaj7

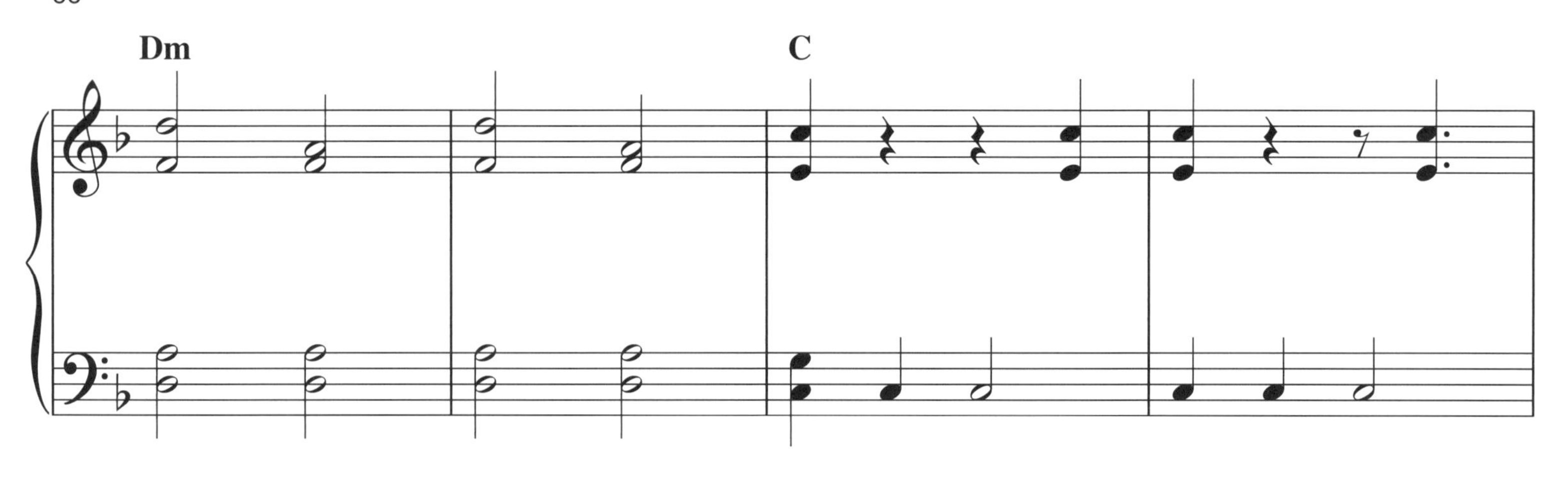
Dm
C

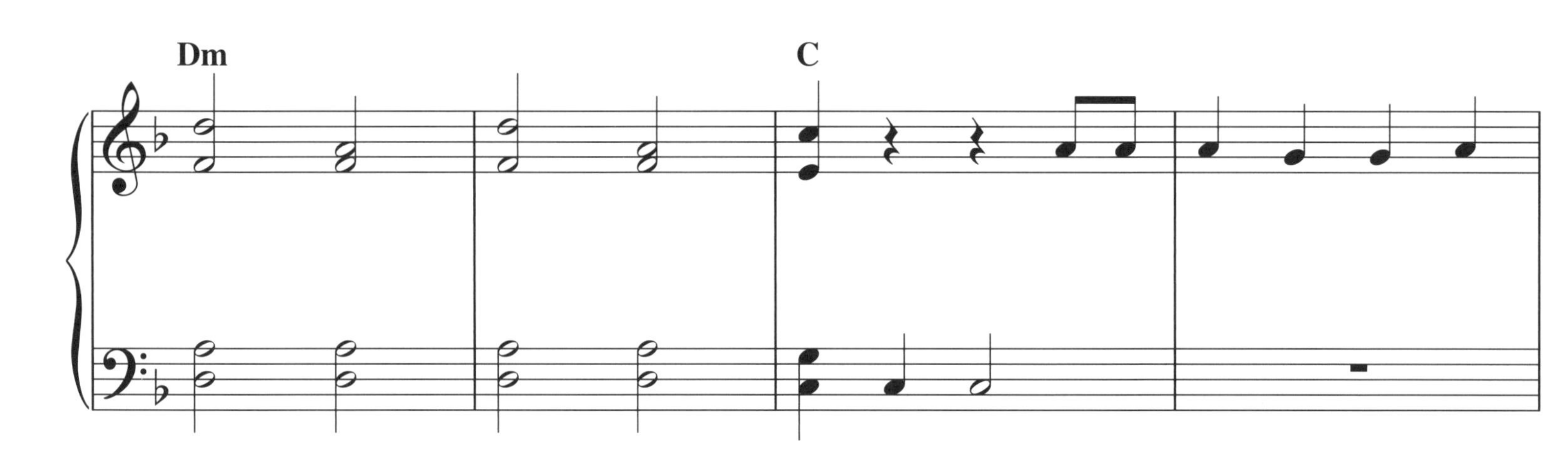
Dm
C

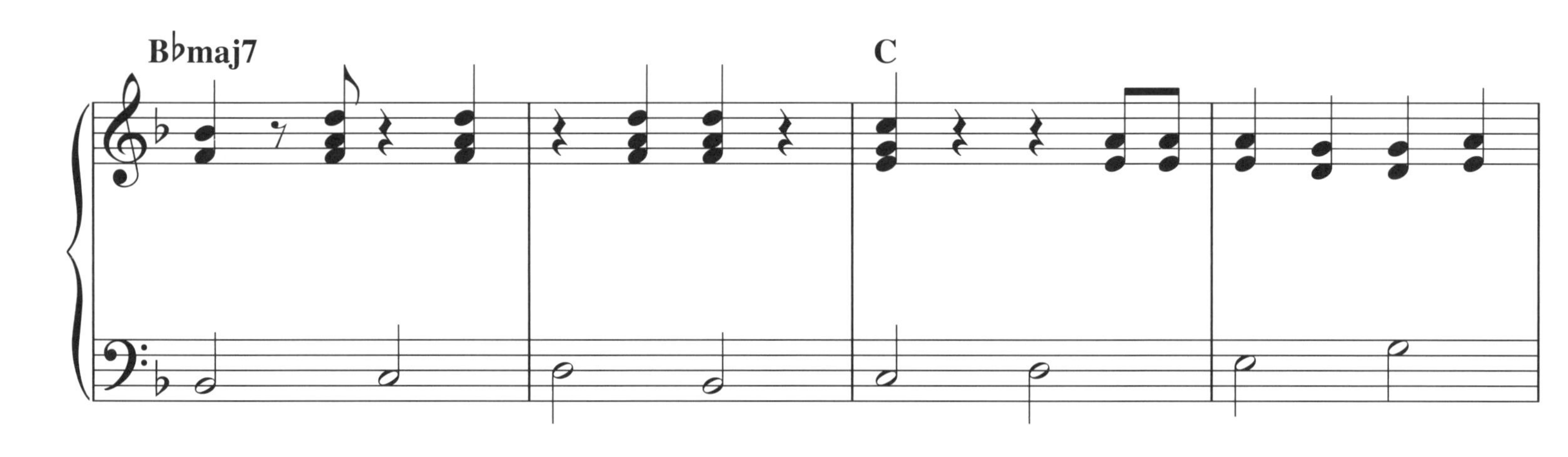
B♭maj7
C

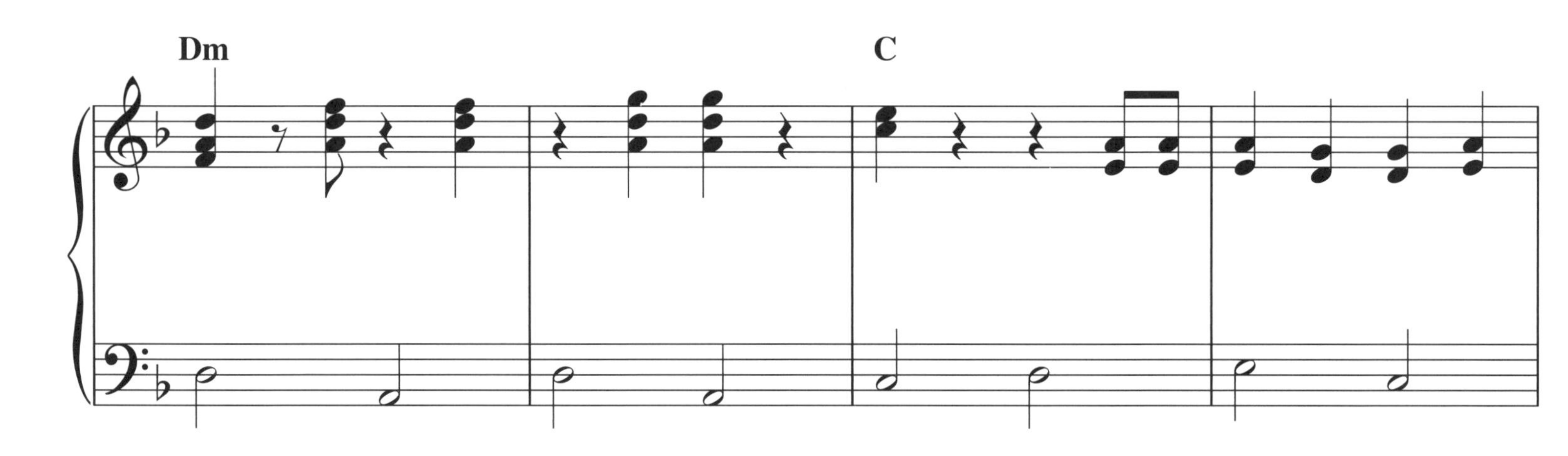
Dm
C

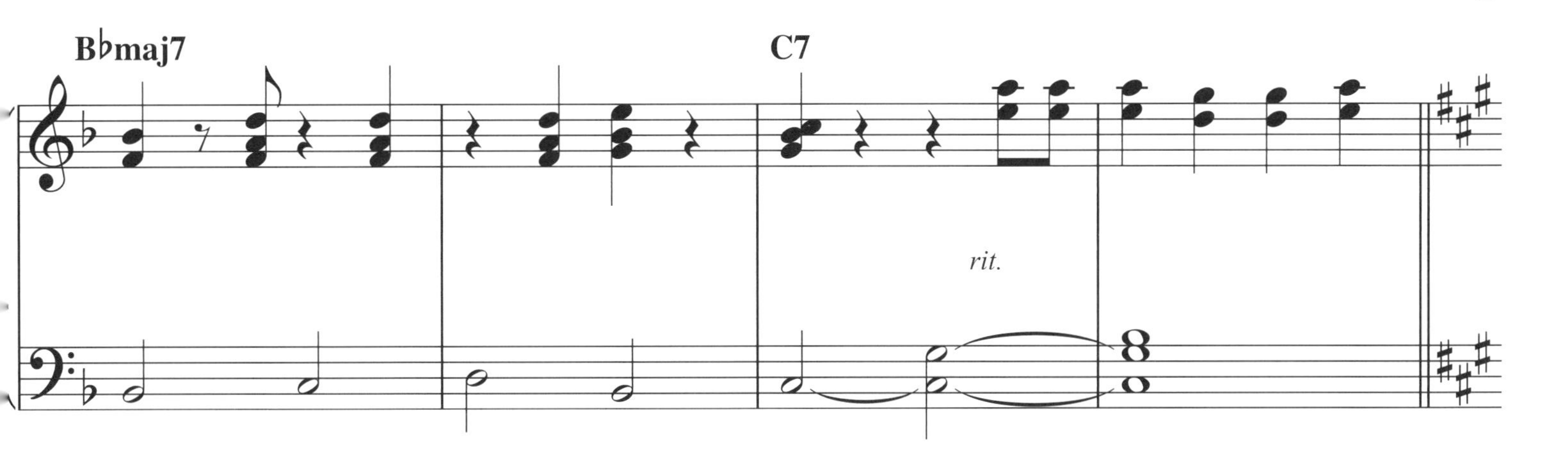
B♭maj7
C7
rit.

Moderately, expressively

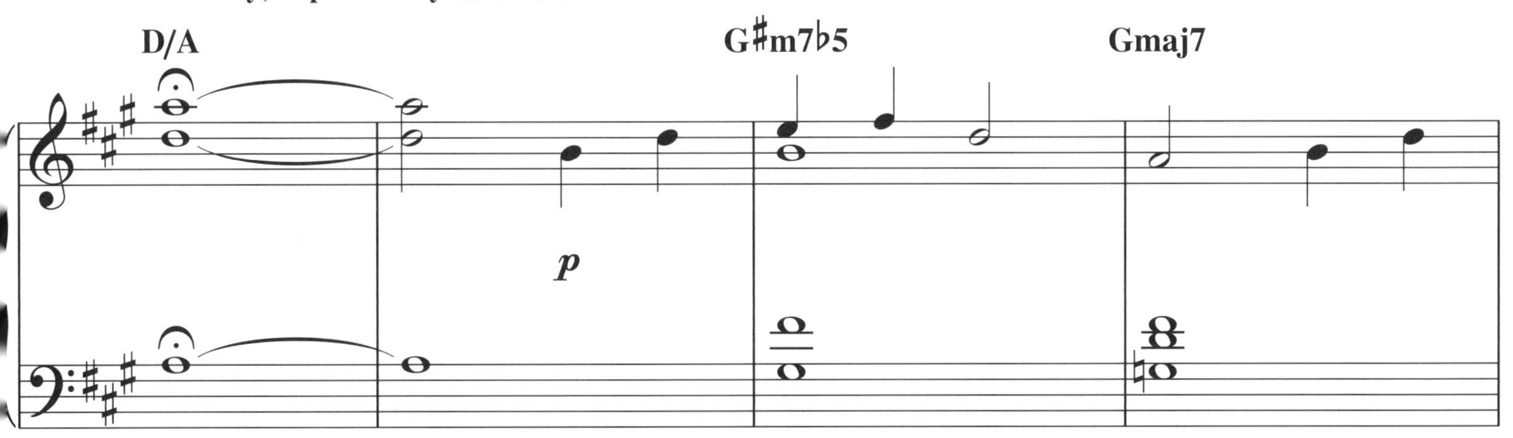
D/A
G♯m7♭5
Gmaj7
p

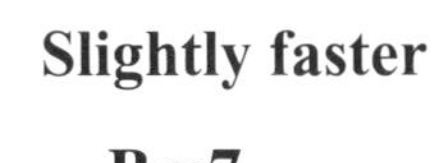
Slightly faster

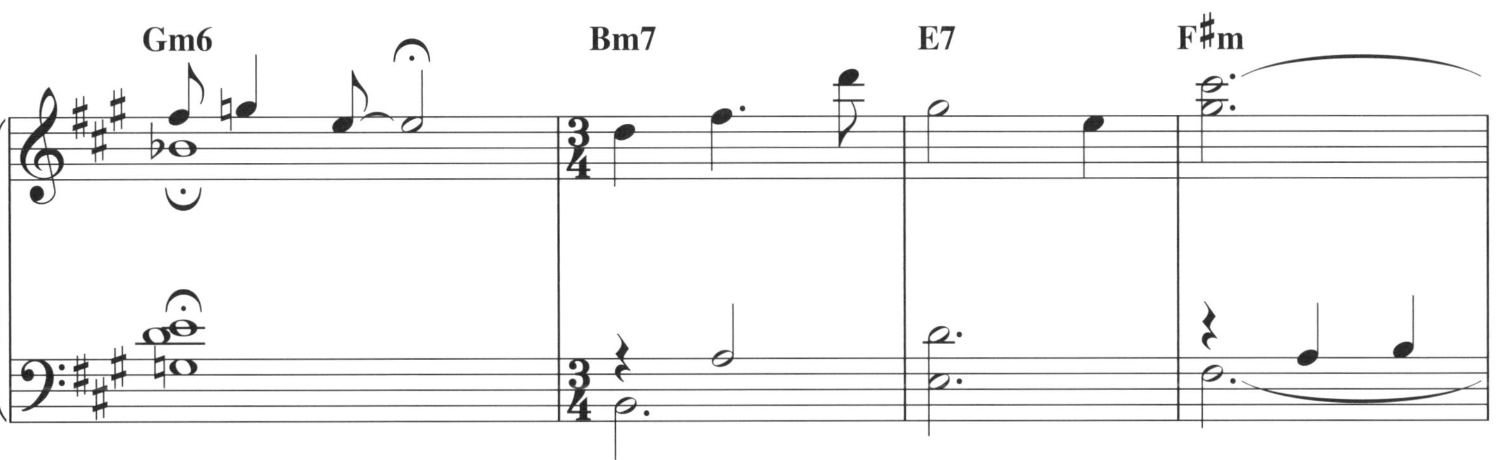
Gm6
Bm7
E7
F♯m

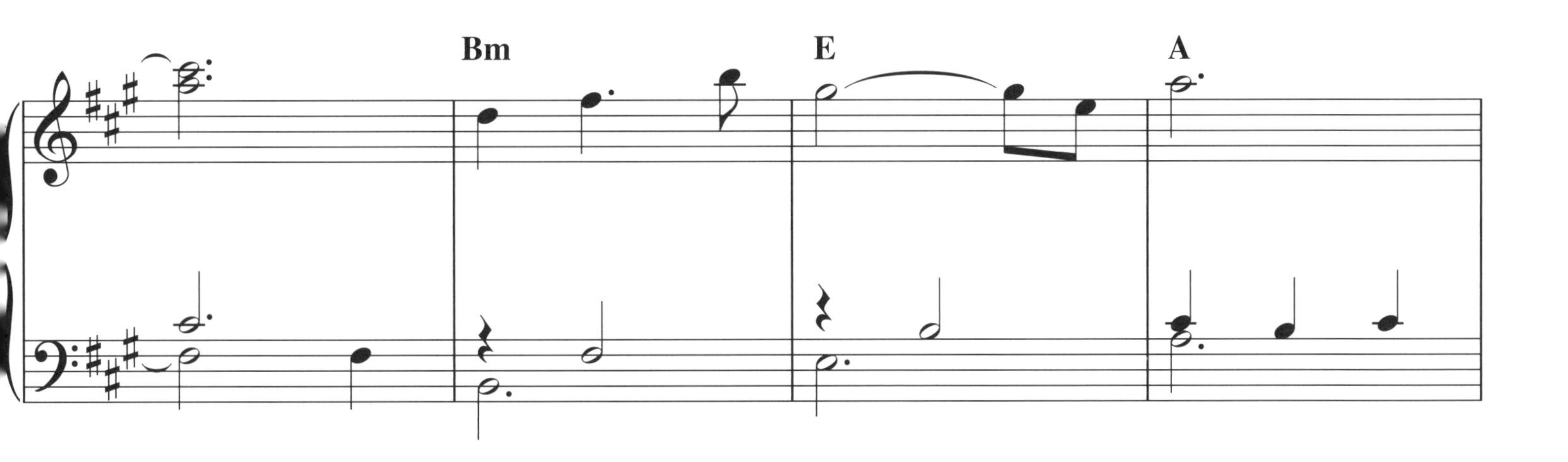
Bm
E
A

Moderately fast Swing
E7/G♯
F♯m
E7
C
mf

C♯dim
Dm

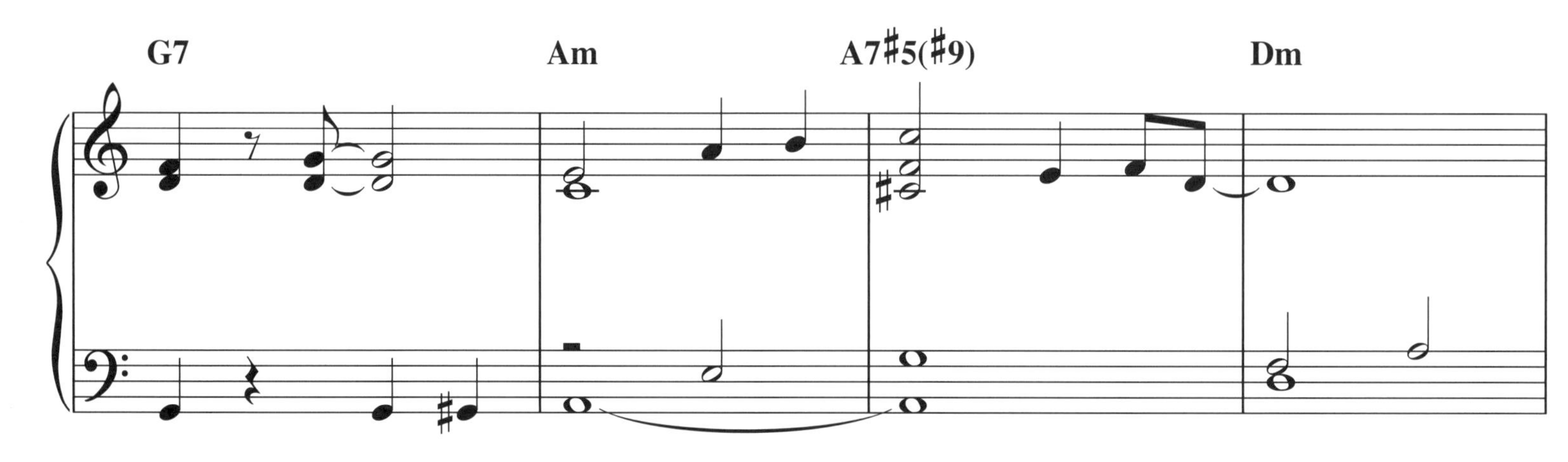
G7
Am
A7♯5(♯9)
Dm

G7(♯5♯9)
C
C♯dim
Dm

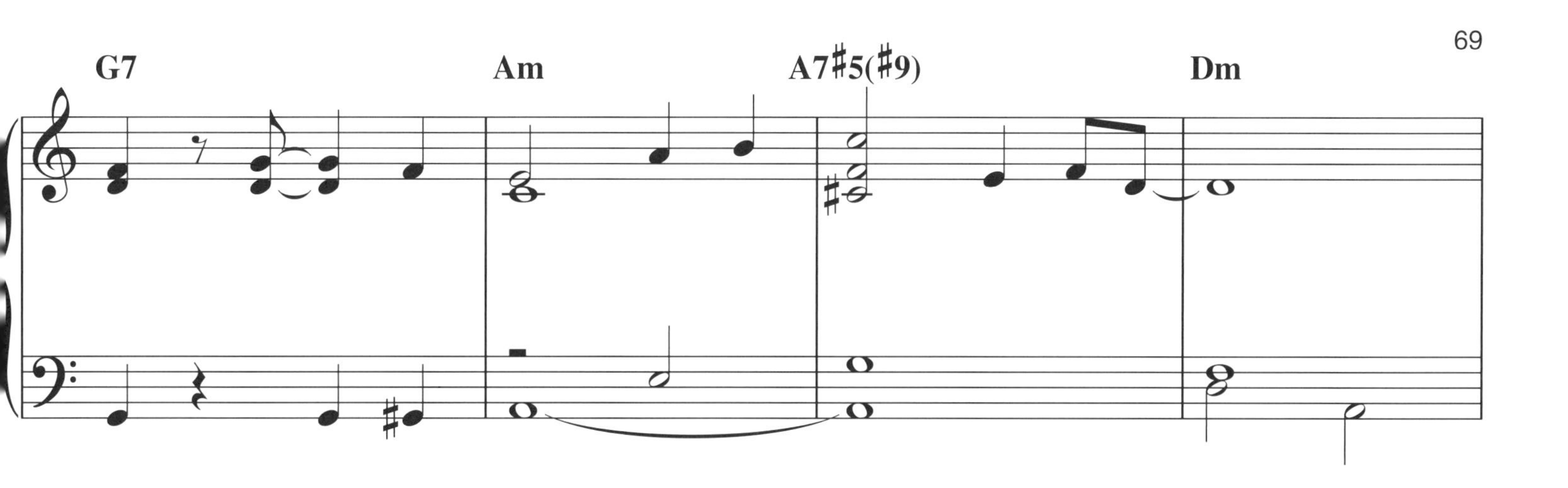
G7
Am
A7♯5(♯9)
Dm

G7
G♯dim7
Am7
D7
Em7

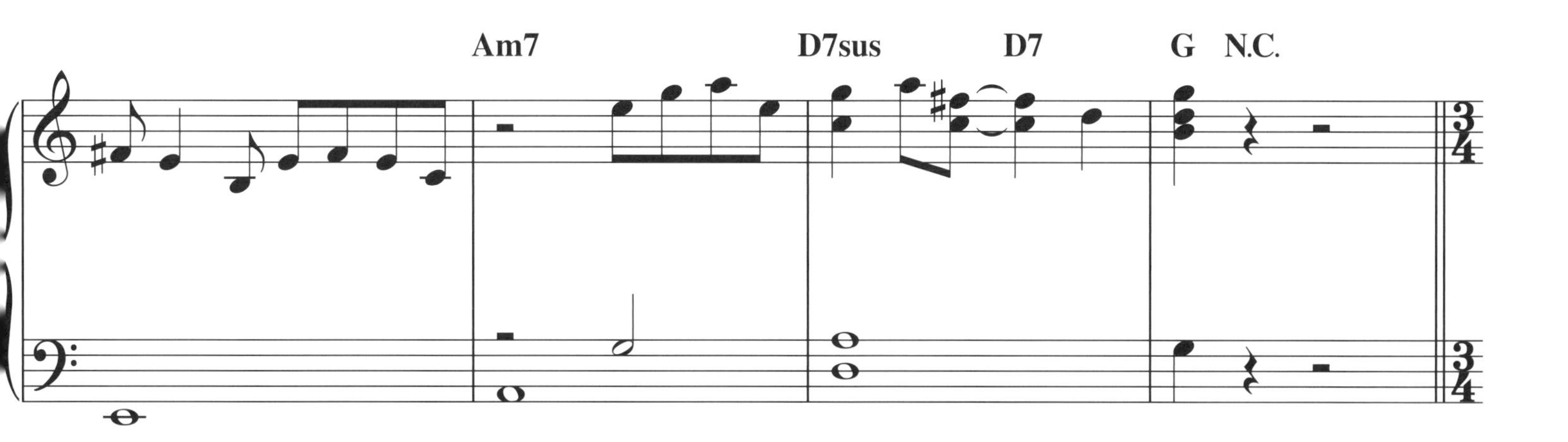
Am7
D7sus
D7
G
N.C.

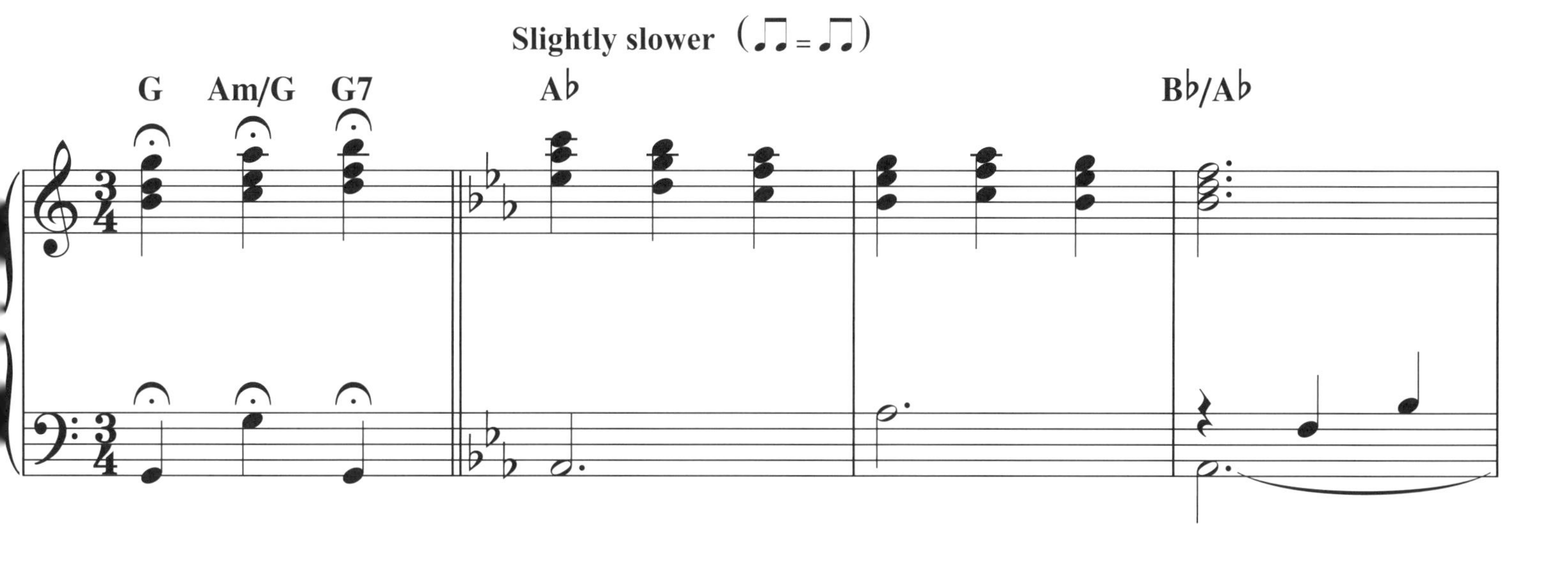
Slightly slower
G
Am/G
G7
A♭
B♭/A♭

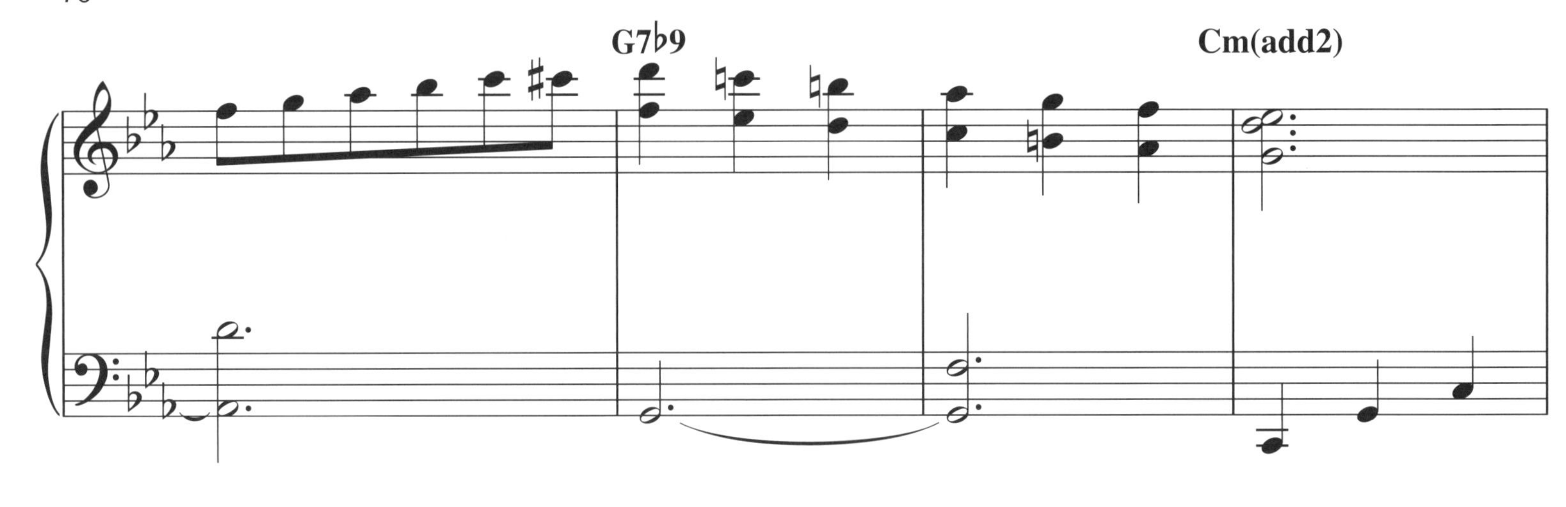
G7♭9
Cm(add2)

Cm
A♭
A♭6
p

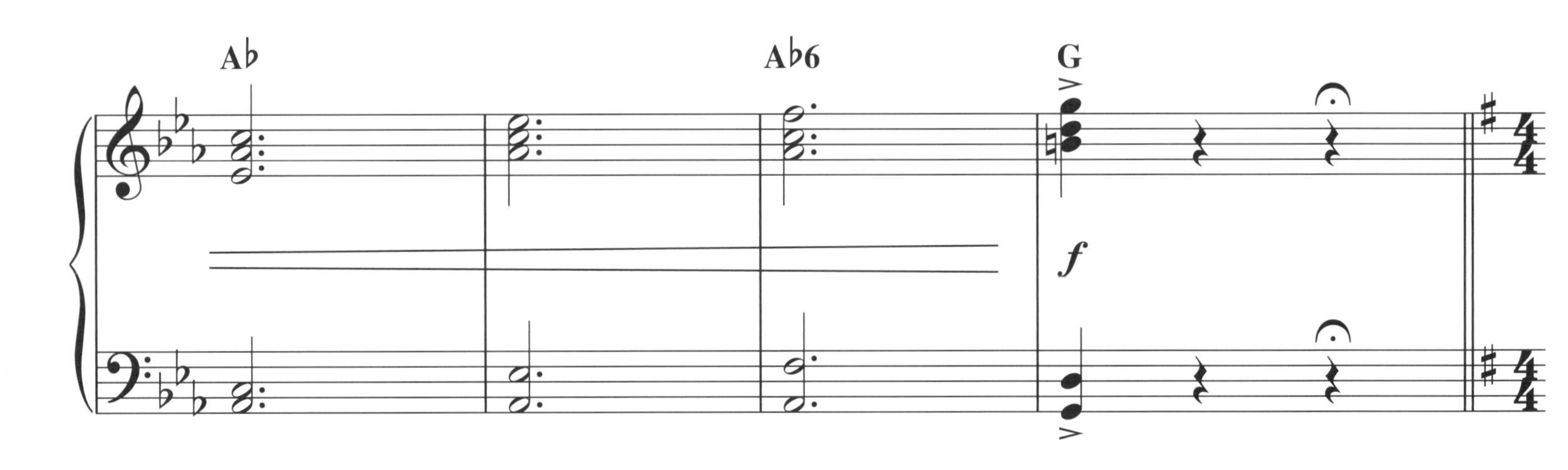
A♭
A♭6
G
f

Moderately

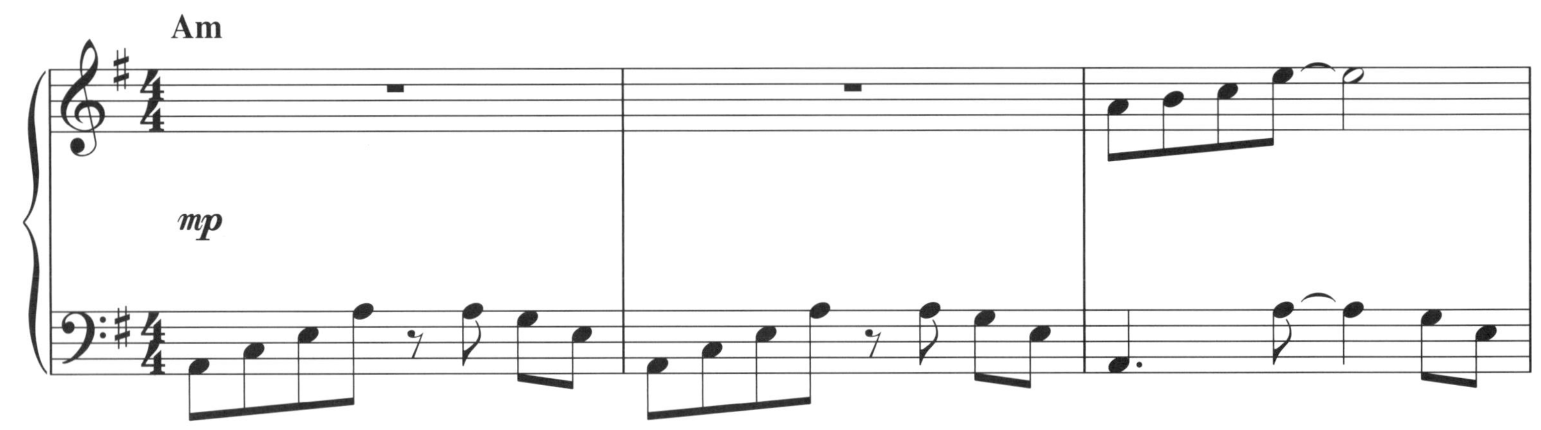
Am
mp

D
D7
Em
Am
D
D7
G
Gmaj7
G
Am
D

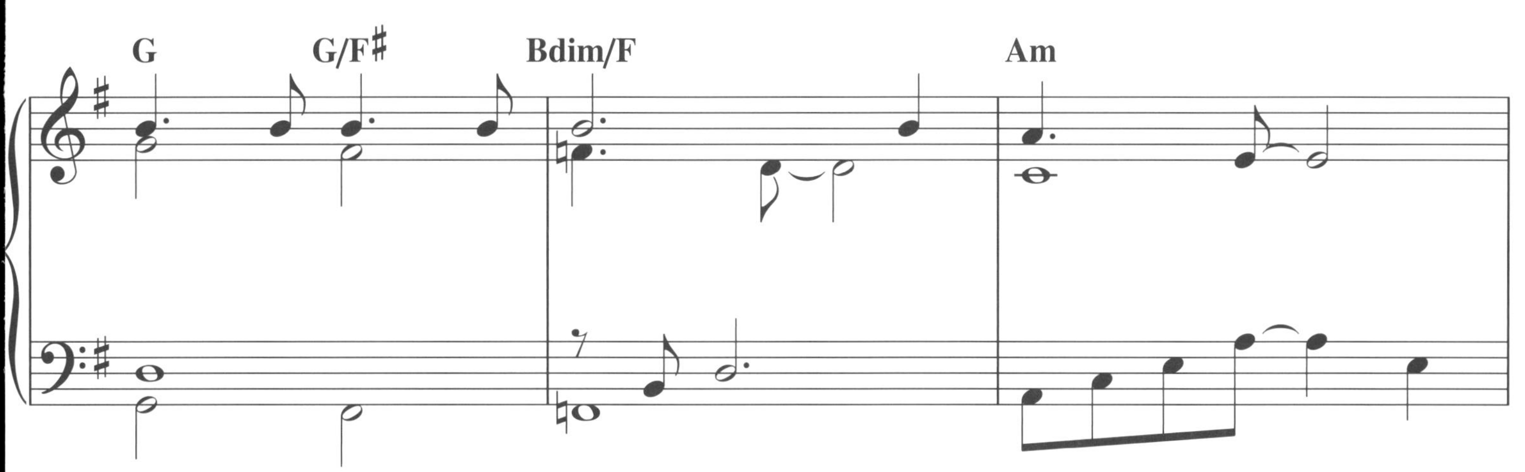
G
G/F♯
Bdim/F
Am

B7
3
Em
Em/D
Am
B7
3
Slowly, very freely
N.C.
p decresc. to end
1.
2.